T. H. Weller

D0403214

WHERE WINTER NEVER COMES

WHERE WINTER

NEVER COMES

A STUDY OF

MAN AND NATURE

IN THE TROPICS

BY

MARSTON BATES

CHARLES SCRIBNER'S SONS, NEW YORK

1952

Contents

Illustrations

WHERE WINTER NEVER COMES

CHAPTER I

*

The Point of View

My wife was rummaging among some old papers the other day, and came across a collection of themes I had written for my Freshman course in English. One of these was entitled "Why I Want to Study Biology in the Tropics"; and except for a certain awkwardness of expression (which I hope has been overcome), it might have been written yesterday. There were all of my basic articles of faith, set down in a clear, schoolboy hand, twenty-seven years ago. The professor had given me an "A"—for the grammar, I suppose, rather than the ideas.

I had forgotten my adolescent ambition to go to the tropics; but sitting there, with this English theme in my hand, the memories came flooding back. I remembered my boyhood explorations in the hammocks of southern Florida, which gave me an intimation of what the real tropical forest might be like. I remembered the articles and books by William Beebe that I came across while I was still in high school; and my first reading of Bates (no relation) on the Amazon and Wallace in the Malay Archipelago. My friends, Sandy Fairchild and Teddy Burgess, went off with Sandy's father to collect butterflies in Panama, and I remembered my envy of their chance to see that marvellous

1

world for themselves. All through college I dreamed of getting a job in the tropics when I was through, and I remembered the thrill when, in my senior year, I got a chance to be a "banana cowboy" with the United Fruit Company.

I filled out all of the papers, got a passport, and reported to the nearest company office, in Havana. And there my beautiful dream collapsed—I failed to pass the physical examination because of a heart murmur. It was a terrible blow, and I crawled back home to spend the next year tutoring local numbskulls in Latin and trigonometry for their College Boards.

I might have accepted this defeat as final, but I was rescued by a resourceful lady who has since become my mother-in-law. She knew the right people, pulled the right strings, and finally persuaded the United Fruit Company to take me despite my continuing failure to meet their physical requirements. So, in September, 1928, I set sail from New York on the S. S. *Carrillo,* bound for Honduras, for my idea of a naturalist's paradise.

For once, realization lived up to expectation, and I spent a happy three years in the forests and banana plantations of the Honduras coast, and as a sort of agricultural extension agent among the coffee planters of the Guatemalan highlands. But it became apparent that to do the things I wanted to do, I needed more education; so, reluctantly, I headed north to Harvard University. I spent much of my time there pointing out how unfavorably Massachusetts compared with Honduras, and at every vacation opportunity I escaped again to the Caribbean. Finally, when I had acquired the degrees that symbolize learning and status among scientists, I threw in my lot with the Rockefeller Foundation, because that organization seemed to offer the finest opportunities for scientific work in really interesting environments.

But I do not intend, in this book, to write an autobiography. I have started on a personal note purely to warn the reader of my bias. I fell in love with the idea of the tropics during a childhood spent in Florida, and I have remained true to that love ever since—within reasonable limits. There was, to be sure, a mild flirtation with the Mediterranean during one period of my life, but I think I loved the Mediterranean only for the ways in which it reminded me of the tropics. And in the winter months, which can be cold enough even in Egypt, my loyalty to the Mediterranean disappeared, and I longed to be back south of the line of Cancer, where winter never comes.

I do not intend to write a travel book, either. There are enough of those, and I think the places where I have lived have already been quite adequately described by many people. There is always room for more accounts of strange places, written by perceptive people who can see old things with new eyes and who, with a magic touch, can transmute the new things into an enrichment of the total experience of the reader. But I doubt whether I have those perceptive eyes or that magic touch; and anyway, I do not want to describe places, or recount adventures, or give my impressions of the quaint customs of native people. Rather, I want to write about ideas, to describe in general terms the characteristics of men and nature in the tropical environment, basing my interpretation on my reading of the thoughts and observations of others as well as on my own experience.

I have long been in rebellion against the toplofty attitude that the Western world is apt to take of the tropics. One expression of this attitude is found in the books of the late Professor Ellsworth Huntington of Yale University, who has written learnedly and at length about the relationships between civilization and climate. He has shown, to his own satisfaction and to that of his many followers, that civilization is a sort of automatic product of the stimulating climate of places like New Haven, Connecticut; and that the poor people who live in the enervating climates of the equatorial regions are forever doomed to eke out their miserable existence, sweating torpidly in the shade of their skimpy palm trees.

Clearly, Professor Huntington did not like warm climates, and he documented his dislike with impressive learning. I happen to love sunshine and warmth, and I can do with them quite happily all of the year round. I should like, then, with my prejudice, to examine this business of climate and civilization, to see what sort of deductions I can draw about the matter.

Alongside the theories of climate and civilization, we have the theories of race and civilization. At the moment, the Aryan myth is rather out of fashion, but still there is often in the Western mind some faint contamination of the belief that those lesser breeds of southern latitudes are not quite capable of the fine accomplishments of Western man. There are, within the tropics, men of all shades of skin color and with every variety of culture and civilization, and I should like to look into the relationships between these.

Finally, we have the question of economic development. The tropics, according to practically everybody, are "backward" or "undeveloped" or, more delicately, "under-developed." Practically everybody also has some idea as to what should be done about this, though there is little unanimity among the opinions. In the simple matter of extent of resources, some authors consider that the hope of the future for all mankind lies in the rich possibilities of places like the Amazon and Congo basins. But others write these off, pointing out that tropical soils are poor, that the tropical climate is impossible, and that tropical peoples are hopelessly lacking in brain power.

I have accumulated a few ideas about this matter of the development of the tropics, and I shall not be happy until I have aired them. More and more, I have become convinced that the difficulty lies not so much in the nature of the tropics, as in the nature of Western civilization. This, after all, developed in Europe and North America under conditions of climate and soil that are quite different from those found in the tropics, and it is consequently not surprising that its techniques of agriculture, medicine and industry have not always automatically fitted into tropical conditions.

Our scientists and philosophers have mostly lived in the north, which they quite naturally have come to regard as the center of the universe. Somehow, in the course of my experience, I have come to take a different view, and to believe that the center of the universe lies not in Europe, but somewhere farther south, between the lines of Capricorn and Cancer. I suspect that most of human evolution took place in the tropics—that our ancestors went through the slow process of change from ape-like to man-like character under genial climatic conditions somewhere in tropical Asia or Africa. I suspect that our first steps in the use of tools took place in the tropics; that man first learned to cultivate plants and domesticate animals in the tropics; that the beginnings of our civilization were either in the tropics, or just outside in the valleys of the Indus, Euphrates or Nile rivers. With this perspective, it seems possible that it is Western civilization, rather than the tropical environment, that is queer.

I have, naturally, many misgivings about my qualifications for embarking on this broad defense of the tropical environment. For one thing, I want to write about people, cultures, civilizations, and to deal with the general concepts of history and geography. But by training and experience, I am a naturalist, and my scientific work has all been with things like butterflies and mosquitoes and the virus of yellow fever.

I think, however, that the point of view of the naturalist or scientist deserves a hearing in the world to-day. He may possibly be able to bring a fresh viewpoint, a slightly different perspective, to the problems that plague us all. The scientist, by virtue of his work, does not gain any special competence in fields outside of his own; but he does, perforce, acquire a rather special attitude and distinctive working methods within his own field, and it may be interesting to have him attempt to carry this attitude and these methods over into other fields. It is, for example, often fruitful to have a biologist take up work in chemistry, or a physicist work in biology, and by the same reasoning it may be useful to have a naturalist look at tropical man.

My aim in this book, then, is to write a natural history of tropical man. Natural history, to me, is about the same thing as ecology, the study of organisms in relation to their environment. This is always a complicated sort of study, because it involves the analysis of all of the varied interrelations among the different kinds of animals and plants that go to make up natural communities, as well as studies of the simpler relationships between single organisms or particular communities with the physical environment of climate and soil.

The ecology of man, however, cannot directly be compared with the ecology of other organisms because, in the case of man, we have to deal with a new sort of factor—culture. This means that we have shifted worlds when we move from the biological to the social sciences, so that any proposition carried from the one to the other must be examined anew in the changed context. It is like moving from physics or chemistry to biology, where the added factor of life changes the perspective, the interest, the methods of study, and the sort of results that may be obtained.

Yet, just as physics and chemistry furnish the necessary background against which biological studies must be built, so I think biology furnishes the necessary background against which social studies must be built. And we must take care that these various fields of inquiry do not really develop as separate worlds, with communication among them increasingly difficult. We need to remember the phenomenon of the interrelatedness of things, to remember that all human knowledge is continuous, and that no part can successfully be cultivated for long as a thing-in-itself. This, at least, is my belief; and written out, I hope that it will serve me, as a naturalist, by way of a passport for travel into the territories of the historians, the anthropologists and the economists.

But I do not want to weigh this book down with too much meaning. I am not trying to write for the historians and economists, but for my fellow citizens who may have some interest in the tropics. And that, today, should mean all of us, because with modern transportation and communication, the world has become a neighborhood and world events have taken on the force and relevance of neighborhood events. What happens in India and Ethiopia and Venezuela can no longer be dismissed as remote, of no concern to us. We may never expect to go there, but our daily lives may be affected by the actions and attitudes of the people who live there, just as our actions and attitudes affect the Venezuelans and the Indians. We have got the seven league boots that once upon a time were but a fairy tale, and the tropics now are just across the street. We cannot dismiss what goes on there as something of no concern to us.

I want to write, then, about man and the environment in the tropics. Inevitably I shall have to write almost as much about Western European civilization as about the tropics. This European culture has had a tremendous influence on all aspects of life in the tropics in the years since Vasco Da Gama first rounded the Cape of Good Hope and found the sea route to India, and since Columbus, searching for another route, first cast anchor off a little island in the Bahamas. It may be well to start with a sketch of this history of European discovery of the tropical region, since the events of that history color all of our relationships with the lands and peoples to the south of us.

It is, for the most part, a sordid, bloody story and there is no use in trying to gloss it over with romance and bravery and high adventure. There were men and incidents that any people could be proud of, but there were more that reflect shame not only on the West, but on all mankind. But we cannot erase the history. It is recorded not only in the books, but in the attitudes and habits and relationships of living people—a past throwing its dark shadow over present searchings for peace and understanding. We cannot erase the history, but we can try to live it down.

After a sketch of this historical background, I think we should look at the kinds of people that live within the tropics—the varieties of tropical man. I plan in that connection to review a little of what we know of the history of human evolution, which seems to me to indicate that man is, essentially, a tropical animal. After discussing man as an animal, we should consider man as a bearer of culture and examine some of the varieties of culture that have been developed in the tropics, with special attention to elements like agriculture that may have originated in the tropics and subsequently influenced man's culture everywhere.

Any general comments on cultures lead directly to a consideration of the special types of cultures that we call civilizations. The tropical civilizations have always fascinated me and I should like to give some general account of the various kinds that were developed both in the Old World and the New. These seem to me, in themselves, to refute the idea that climate is a direct cause of civilization; but before considering the relationships between climate and culture, we shall need a chapter on the general nature of tropical climates.

After that we can look at man's physical and cultural adaptations to climate. Since an important factor in the man-climate relationship is clothing, I should like to give this a good deal of attention. I am so impressed with the importance of clothing as a "good thing" in northern climates and a "bad thing" in tropical climates, that I have come to feel that in this present world it is almost true that "clothes make the man." This matter of clothing habits brings up the general problem of the effect of the transfer of culture traits from one environment into another, and of the apparent failure of European culture to flourish in the tropical environment. I suspect that this failure is a consequence of the nature of the European civilization (including clothing), which makes this civilization the real "burden" of the white man when he tries to live in the tropics.

The tropical environment, of course, offers many distinctive problems for man, and we are apt to give first place among these to tropical diseases, which consequently should be discussed in a separate chapter. The food habits of man also show special relations with the environment, because different kinds of food are available under different circumstances, and I think this also deserves separate treatment.

I said that I wanted to write a natural history of tropical man, which meant a study of man and environment; yet in this sketch I have included far more about man than about environment. I shall attempt to remedy this in a general chapter on tropical nature, followed by two chapters giving special attention to the distinctive characteristics of tropical forests and tropical seas. Since man's interest in nature is primarily as a "resource" to be exploited, this economic aspect of the tropical environment should be given separate attention.

For the most part, I intend to avoid discussion of human social organization, since this seems to offer no special peculiarities in relation to the tropical environment. But the utilization of tropical resources is intimately related to the national and colonial organization of government within the tropics, and some discussion of this would seem to be required, if only to draw attention to the nature of the problem.

My hope in this book is to make some contribution to the understanding, by northern peoples, of the nature of the problems of man and civilization in the tropics. My final chapter, then, may appropriately be devoted to a review of these problems of understanding in our planetary neighborhood, especially with regard to the efforts of Western governments to extend the benefits of the technologies and industries that have developed within their civilization to the peoples and civilizations that lie within the tropics, within the area marked off on our maps by the lines of Capricorn and Cancer.

But our first step will be to look at the element of history in the relationship between the West and the tropics. As with so much of Western history, this will take us back to the Greeks, who first had the idea of drawing the lines of the tropics on their maps.

CHAPTER II

★

The Element of History

THE word "tropic" comes from the Greek *tropikos,* meaning the solstice, which is based on *trope,* a turning. The tropic marks the time when the sun turns back in its annual north-south migration of path and hence, by easy extension, also the place of the turning, the farthest north and farthest south that the sun at noon is ever directly overhead.

The annual shift in the path of the sun, with the corresponding changes in length of day, is caused by the angle that the spinning earth holds in its journey around the sun. If the polar axis of the earth were exactly perpendicular to the plane of the earth's orbit around the sun, the sun would always be directly overhead at noon at the equator, and the angle of its rays would increase evenly toward either pole. But the polar axis is tilted, so that the earth's equator forms an angle with the plane of the earth's orbit around the sun (called the "obliquity of the ecliptic" by the astronomers). This angle changes slowly and slightly over the centuries, and it has a value nowadays of about $23° 27'$. Thus, in the course of the earth's annual journey around the sun, the direct rays gradually move upward to a limit about 23½ degrees north of the equator, then downward to the corresponding southern limit.

Since the circuit of the earth around the sun defines our solar year, these shifts in the path of the sun's direct rays give the frame for our calendar. The summer solstice, when the direct rays strike the Tropic of Cancer, when the day is longest in the North Temperate zone, and the sun can be seen all night north of the Arctic circle, falls on June 21st. The winter solstice, when everything is opposite, falls on December 21st. The midpoints, when the sun passes over the equator, are called the equinoxes.

These calendar events were worked out in great detail early in the history of man, perhaps quite independently in various places. They were important because the changes of the sun and of the "fixed" stars marked the planting times, the harvesting times, the flood times of the rivers, the times for festivals in honor of the controlling gods. Surely some of the early priests worked out the relation between the celestial events of the calendar, and the geographical events on the surface of the earth, but our direct knowledge of this relation dates only from the Greeks.

The Babylonians were knowledgeable astronomers and we have inherited from them the system whereby the circle is divided into 360 degrees, which still controls our geographical measurements, and we know that they had worked out the details of the calendar problem. They divided the year into twelve periods according to the timing of the appearance of twelve groups of fixed stars, which has passed on to us in the signs of the zodiac (though with Latin names). Thus on June 21st the constellation of the crab (*cancer* in Latin) rises and sets with the sun and is invisible throughout the night. On December 21st, this happens with the constellation of the horned goat (*capricorn*).

The Greeks surely learned much from these Babylonians, perhaps mostly by way of the Phoenicians; but they were careless about giving credit to barbarians. Some member of the Pythagorean school, about 525 B.C., developed the theory that the earth was spherical, instead of flat. Aristarchus, about 270 B.C., worked out a description of the planetary revolution of the earth around the sun, bringing astronomy to a point that it did not

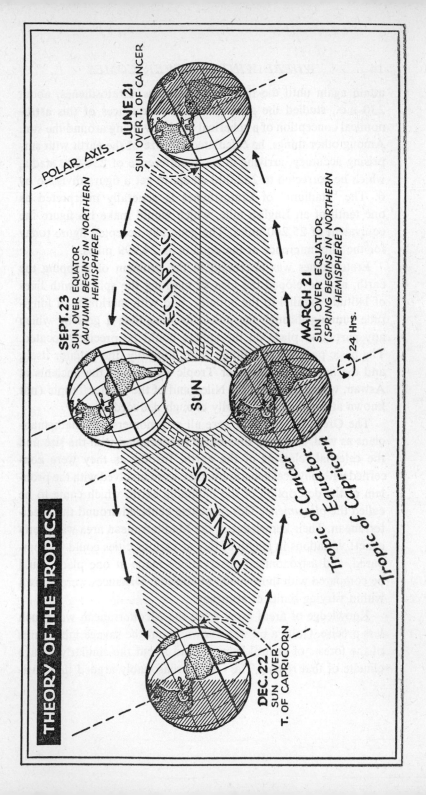

THEORY OF THE TROPICS

POLAR AXIS

JUNE 21
SUN OVER T. OF CANCER

SEPT. 23
SUN OVER EQUATOR
(AUTUMN BEGINS IN NORTHERN
HEMISPHERE)

MARCH 21
SUN OVER EQUATOR
(SPRING BEGINS IN NORTHERN
HEMISPHERE)

ECLIPTIC

SUN

24 Hrs.

Tropic of Cancer
Tropic of Equator
Tropic of Capricorn

PLANE OF

DEC. 22
SUN OVER
T. OF CAPRICORN

attain again until the time of Copernicus. Eratosthenes, about 230 B.C., studied the geographical consequences of this astronomical conception of a spherical earth revolving around the sun. Among other things, he calculated the size of the earth with surprising accuracy, arriving at a circumference of 250,000 stadia, which he corrected to 252,000 stadia to get a figure divisible by 6. The "stadium" of Eratosthenes is generally interpreted as one tenth of an English mile, which would make his figure the equivalent of 25,200 miles. The generally accepted figure today for the circumference at the equator is 24,999 miles.

Eratosthenes was interested in the problem of mapping the earth, and developed the idea of marking the sphere with lines of latitude parallel to the equator, and with meridians of longitude running through the poles, forming thus a grid by which any particular place on the sphere could be precisely located. The basic parallels of latitude were, logically, the equator itself, and the lines of the Summer Tropic (known to the ancients at Aswan, where it crossed the Nile) and of the Winter Tropic (not known at first hand, but easily enough deduced).

The Greek geographers were all astronomers and mathematicians as well, and were thus much preoccupied with the size and the celestial relations of the earth. Insofar as they were concerned with physical geography, they were involved with the problem of the description of the habitable earth, which came to be called the *oikoumene*. This of course centered around the Mediterranean. Their knowledge of the Mediterranean area was pretty exact: variations in length of day at various cities could be compared, and astronomical observations made at one place could be compared with those made at another. Distances were known within varying limits of accuracy.

Knowledge of areas away from the Mediterranean was much less precise. Quite a bit was known about the savage inhabitants of the forests of central Europe, and about the similarly savage climate of that region. The Greeks reasonably argued that civilization would hardly be possible in such unfavorable latitudes. About lands farther north, information was increasingly scanty. There were accounts of the perpetually frozen seas to the north of Thule, but these accounts were not verified.

The oikoumene extended immensely and indefinitely to the east, to vaguely known China and Japan, India and Ceylon. To the south, this habitable earth was abruptly limited by the Sahara, but the Land of Cinnamon could be reached by sailing down the Red Sea, providing a basis for conjecture about the general habitability of the equatorial regions.

The astronomical knowledge provided these geographers with a sphere upon which they could orient the oikoumene. This sphere, according to the calculations of Eratosthenes, had a circumference of 25,200 miles; and the oikoumene, precisely known around the Mediterranean and vaguely known across Asia, made a rather small splotch on this spherical surface. Ptolemy reduced the circumference to 18,000 miles (which performed the useful service of misleading Columbus 1200 years later); but this still left most of the sphere blank. It was, they presumed, covered by the circumambient ocean.

On the quadrant of the sphere available for observation, from the equator to the north pole and from the Azores to Asia, they drew lines of latitude parallel to the equator, which divided the oikoumene into zones which, because of the incline of the spherical surface, they called *climata* (*klima,* slope; *klinein,* to slope). Their handiest method of determining the latitude of a particular place, its distance from the equator, was by measuring the number of hours in the longest day of the year. Two cities with the same maximum length of day were thus found to be at equal distances from the equator, in the same clima.

It was, of course, an easy step to observe the other differences associated with differences in length of day, particularly the temperature differences. And from this has grown the whole conception that is now carried by our word *climate.*

The geographers differed in the number of climata that they recognized, and there is no point in going into the historical details here. All schemes involved the basic lines of latitude that we still use, the equator, the tropic and the arctic circle. And the oikoumene was divided by those lines into three broad zones which acquired names based on temperature rather than length of day: the torrid, the temperate and the frigid.

This nomenclature has long bothered me, but it is understandable from the point of view of the Greek geographers who first worked it out. Of "torrid," my dictionary says "parched . . . arid and hot . . . so hot as to scorch." Which is a poor description of the tropics. But the Greeks knew the Tropic of Cancer at the place where that line crosses the Nile at Aswan in Upper Egypt. Anyone who has spent much time at Aswan will agree that "torrid" is fairly applied. With such conditions known at the line of the tropic itself, it is not surprising that the Greeks doubted the possibility of life continuing even further south, in the vicinity of the equator.

The word "temperate" bothers me even more. It is a fair description of Rhodes or Athens or even Alexandria. But we have extended it now to include Minnesota, Connecticut and much of Siberia. To apply "temperate" to a climate where a man may suffer from heat prostration at one time, and be a victim of frostbite a few months later, seems singularly inappropriate. I finally hit on the solution of this naming problem the other day. All that is needed is the prefix "in-". Under the label "Intemperate Zone," the characteristics of the vast region bounded on the south by the Tropic of Cancer and on the north by the Arctic Circle fall into proper perspective. And Patagonia and Tasmania appropriately become a part of the South Intemperate Zone.

There was a real continuity of ideas from the Greeks and Romans through the Moslem scholars and some of the medieval Christians to the Europe of the 15th century. But we tend to dismiss this intervening period under some such label as the

"Dark Ages," and in our folklore it was Columbus, not Eratosthenes or Hipparchus, who proved that the earth was round. Tracing the continuity now is a task of scholarship, and we have to "discover" what the Greeks knew about geography because their knowledge, in this respect at least, has ceased to be a part of our consciously maintained tradition, of our folk memory.

Geographical discovery for us means discovery by Westerners for incorporation in the accepted body of Western knowledge. Pharaoh Necho sent a Phoenician expedition around Africa about 600 B.C., thus discovering for the Egyptian world that Africa could be circumnavigated. But a Portuguese, Bartholomeu Diaz, had to discover this all over again for the Western world in 1488. Columbus discovered the West Indies for the Western world, not for the Carib Indians who had been living there for centuries. Similarly, Captain Cook later discovered the Hawaiian Islands for the West, although their Polynesian inhabitants had been navigating all over the Pacific for several hundreds of years.

There is no use in laboring the point, except that I want to emphasize that discovery is always conditional, and that in our own history books we are always writing about discovery by and for Westerners. This is quite different from discovery by and for Arabs, Chinese or Mayas; hence, history written from another cultural point of view would look quite different, even though equally "true."

European history, however, began to affect the whole surface of the planet in the years around 1500. Looked at with the long perspective of the development of human culture and civilization, it seems as though Europe exploded at that time, spewing its men and ideas all over the globe. The task of the historian of the preceding centuries is to untangle and analyse the various developments that, in their coincidence, made such an explosion possible.

All sorts of things were happening in the years between the first crusades and the first voyage of Columbus, and probably all of them were relevant in some way to the development of the characteristics of Western civilization that led to its rapid global expansion. There were technical developments in shipbuilding and navigation and in the arts of warfare, there were developments in both secular and religious ideas, and surely also there were powerful developments of political and economic forces that found their outlet in the geographical explosion. Interpretation of the geographical explosion in terms of any single cause is surely misleading; but of the complex of forces that were operating, the economic elements are perhaps most easily understood, and the whole movement of geographical exploration is sometimes explained in terms of the development of the spice trade.

It is difficult for us now to realize the importance of spices in the medieval economy. Cattle were kept through the winter with great difficulty, so most of the animals had to be slaughtered in the fall and the meat preserved as best one could. Spices were found to be a great aid in meat preservation, and an even greater aid in making the rotting meat palatable. Spices also became the basic medicines, and many of them still linger on in our pharmacopeia.

Spices from the Orient were important enough in all of the ancient Mediterranean civilizations, but their use spread and multiplied over the rest of Europe with the movement of people and trade that was associated with the crusades. During the 13th and 14th centuries, Venice gradually gained a virtual monopoly of this immensely lucrative trade because of its strategic position in the protected lagoons at the head of the Adriatic, and because of the cleverness and daring of its merchants and politicians. All of Europe was in effect paying tribute to Venice and to its Asiatic allies, enabling the Venetians to build up one of the most opulent societies ever known. The other powers were, naturally, anxious to find any means of breaking this Venetian monopoly; and in the end, they succeeded.

The history of European exploration and exploitation in the tropics can then be regarded as the history of the spice trade, with the initiative in the trade passing from Venice to Spain and Portugal and later to Holland and England, with each nation's role and time determined by a whole complex of political and economic factors. The personal element surely also entered in: the fact that Prince Henry was a Portuguese; that a Spaniard, Isabella, listened to Columbus; or that Elizabeth, Queen of England, was ambitious. The personal element—perhaps unfortunately—makes the most interesting reading.

The first of the famous modern travelers was a Venetian, Marco Polo; but curiously he is about the only famous Venetian traveler. For one thing, Venice was completely absorbed in the traffic of the Mediterranean itself. She faced East, where she dealt first with the power of the Byzantine Empire and then with that of the Moslems. From these she accepted the goods that she passed on to the rest of Christendom, but she could not go beyond these powers to the Indies themselves, the tropical source of her trade materials. For another thing the Venetians were merchants, not writers; and rather uncommunicative merchants, at that. They must have learned quite a deal about the original sources of their spices, precious woods, jewels and silks; but this was treated as secrets of trade rather than as information to be contributed to the general fund of knowledge.

The Polos lived in the 13th century. Soon after the close of this century, travel between Europe and the East became very difficult because of the breakup of the power of the Mongol Khans, and because of the development, across the route of travel, of the empire of the Ottoman Turks. This shift in political conditions in Asia eventually caused the control of the spice trade to pass from the hands of the central Mediterranean powers (Venice and Genoa) to Atlantic Portugal and, with the expulsion of the Moors, to Spain. That these Atlantic powers were able to gain the initiative may have been due, in large part, to a rather remarkable personality, "Prince Henry, the Navigator," who lived from 1394 to 1460. Henry, more than anyone else, built up the Portuguese mastery of seamanship that enabled Bartholomeu Diaz de Novaes to discover the Cape of Good Hope in 1488, and Vasco da Gama to round the Cape and find the sea route to India in 1497–98.

Prince Henry is a tantalizing figure. With the information available, it is impossible to decide whether he was one of those extraordinary individuals who, through the force of their genius, shape the events of an era of history; or whether an extraordinary era of history found its personification in this particular man. The third son of King John of Portugal, Prince Henry became a leader in the wars against the Moors, distinguishing himself in the capture of Ceuta in Algiers in 1415. In conquering the Moors, he also learned something of their science and commerce, and of the vastness and richness of the African lands that lay beyond them to the south. He seems to have realized what possibilities here were open to Portugal, and to have understood the disciplined and slow acquisition of knowledge that would be needed for the exploitation of the Portuguese advantage.

At any rate, he set up an astronomical observatory on the headland of Sagres in the year 1420, and organized a "school" of navigation, chart-making, and cosmographical studies under one Master Jacome of Majorca. A long series of expeditions was sent out southward along the coast of Africa and westward to and perhaps beyond the Azores, the captains being required to prepare detailed charts of their sailings and notes on everything that they observed. Year by year, the captains ventured farther, learned more about navigation on the high seas. In 1434 Cape Bojador, beyond the Canary Islands, was passed; in 1436, Cape Blanco, below the Tropic of Cancer, was reached; and in 1441 a load of slaves and gold dust was brought back from the Guinea coast, which put these explorations on a paying basis for the first time.

Henry seems to have taken up the Guinea trade and slaving with enthusiasm, more than thirty ships sailing between 1444 and 1446. When Henry died, in 1460, his captains had not yet got within 600 miles of the equator; but they had learned to sail in the tropics, learned that a vertical sun at noon did not mean scorching and fatal heat; and they had acquired a sort of faith that the secrets of the seas could gradually be revealed for Portugal's fortune by this slow and dogged system of ever longer sailings.

The great triumph, the complete passage of the tropics and the rounding of the Cape of Good Hope, did not come until the voyage of Bartholomeu Diaz in 1487 and 1488. Diaz sailed on beyond the Cape far enough to be sure that the tip of the continent had been rounded; then, yielding to the clamoring of his men, he turned about and returned home. Diaz had shown the Portuguese the way to the riches of the East, though he was given no particular recognition or reward and when the expedition was organized to test this open route to the Indies, the command was given not to Diaz, but to Vasco da Gama—who apparently was an astute politician as well as a great navigator.

Da Gama sailed with four specially built ships on July 8th, 1497. On November 7th they stopped in St. Helena bay and managed a misunderstanding with the Hottentots. The Cape was rounded by the end of the month and Natal reached by Christmas (whence the name). By April they were off Mozambique and in the region of the regular trade routes between Africa and India—new to Western Europe, but routine to the Moslem World. Here da Gama, by his highhanded cruelty, managed to alienate several local sheiks; but he had the good luck in the end to get a really skilled Arab pilot from the sheik of Malindi, and after an uneventful voyage of 23 days across the Indian Ocean, the fleet came to anchor on May 22nd, off the city of Calicut on the Malabar Coast.

The West had met the ancient East. And it is significant for the future of the relationship that this first contact was made by one of the most arrogant and cruel leaders that the West has ever produced. The whole bloody story of this Portuguese adventure in the spice trade has been told in a recent book by Henry Hart, called *Sea Road to the Indies*. One incident from da Gama's second voyage may serve to illustrate his character, and to illuminate the nature of the Portuguese-Indian understanding.

"To impress the samorin [of Calicut] that he meant to follow up his ultimatum with action, the admiral perpetrated another inexcusable and inhuman outrage. On the arrival of the fleet a number of fishermen had put out in their boats to sell their catch to the crews. Gama had thirty-eight of the poor innocent fellows seized. Protesting and struggling, they were dragged on the ship and hanged from the yard-arms. At the same time Gama ordered his ships to bombard the city, which possessed but few, if any, cannon with which to reply.

"At nightfall Gama ordered the bodies of the hanged men taken down. Their heads, hands, and feet were cut off and heaped up in a boat, and their dismembered bodies were flung overboard to be washed inshore by the tide. A message in Arabic was fastened to the heap of hands, feet and heads, pointing out that this was but a warning and a forecast of the fate of the city if it resisted. Correa adds that the letter suggested that the samorin make a fine curry of the severed heads and limbs. The boat was then cast off to drift ashore."

But the whole story of the explorations of the Portuguese and the Spaniards in the 16th century is too well known to need recapitulation here: the four voyages of Columbus; Balboa's jaunt across Panama to a view of the Pacific; Cortes' conquest of Mexico; the circumnavigation of the globe by one of the ships that started out, in 1519, under Magellan's command; Pizarro's conquest of Peru, and so on through the bloody, looting century.

From the beginning the process of discovery and exploration

has had a profound effect on the peoples "discovered" and the regions "explored." The tropical regions that we see today have everywhere been modified to a greater or lesser extent by the migrations of European peoples and by the expansion of Western civilization, so that it is very difficult to put together a picture of these lands as they must have appeared before Columbus blundered into the West Indies or da Gama found his way around the Cape of Good Hope. Yet, without this picture, how are we to judge how much of the present is due to this explosion of Western Europe, and how much to the characteristics of the tropical regions themselves?

Each tropical region has reacted to the European contact in a distinct and characteristic way. In America, the local civilizations tumbled on contact with the Europeans, like so many houses of cards; and in some places, like the West Indies, even the people themselves disappeared. A new sort of culture, that of Latin America, was built on the wreck of these peoples and civilizations. At first the new civilization was purely colonial, but gradually it assumed an independent character under the influence of local conditions and with the gradual resurgence of indigenous cultural elements like those of the art of Mexico.

In Asia, the local civilizations at first maintained both cultural and political independence, resisting the brutal arrogance of the first European "discoverers," though yielding to the temptations of trade. But the Europeans gradually gained political dominance over most of tropical Asia through a series of bloody maneuvers among themselves and the various regional sovereignties; the story of the Portuguese, the Spaniards, the English, the Dutch and, last of all, the French and the Germans, in this region, is long, complicated and disgraceful. Cultural resistance has been stronger, however, than political resistance, and the regional civilizations have maintained a sort of continuity despite the European onslaughts. Christianity, for instance, which is generally considered to be the most important European cultural export, has made little progress, though the region has been swept by other proselytizing religions like Buddhism and Mohammedanism.

In Africa the tropical people, at the time of European contact, had not developed any indigenous civilization. Nevertheless, they showed a surprising cultural and physical resistance—not melting away like the American Indians. I suspect that this difference was partly a matter of disease. The Europeans brought a whole lot of new diseases to America, which helped greatly in finishing off the Indians; in Africa, however, local diseases like yellow fever, malaria, sleeping sickness and so forth, managed frequently to finish off the Europeans who tried to live in the place. In the end, the Europeans decided that "the climate was unhealthy," and restricted their African enterprises to exploitive forays by administrators and traders. These might have a disruptive enough effect on local cultural patterns, but they could not result in the development of a totally new pattern like that which has emerged in Latin America.

In Australia, to complete this tour, the local people melted away before the Europeans, as did the American Indians of the West Indies and of the United States, leaving an empty space in which a transplant of European culture could be established. The Australian situation is most closely comparable with that of the United States; and it is also essentially a Temperate Zone culture though with a large tropical extension in Queensland. This Queensland area is of particular interest to any student of the tropics because it provides a unique opportunity to study the effect of a tropical environment on an English culture and European population.

The documentation of discovery and exploration, of the first culture contacts between Europe and the tropical regions, is deplorably fragmentary, despite its volume. I presume that all of the exploring ships kept logs, and many of these as well as journals of individual members of expeditions have been preserved and published. This represents an enormous mass of material that has not been fully exploited by modern scholars—mostly because sorting out and interpreting the relevant observations is such a tedious job.

These early explorers, of course, did not keep journals with the sort of observations that we would like to have, because the system of making such observations had not yet been invented. There was not even a method of preserving historical or natural specimens, since museums and systematic collections did not exist. Of course the explorers carried back curiosities to show their princes the marvels of the new lands. But these were exhibited, admired, and then forgotten with the advent of the next marvel. The curiosities, if made of gold or some other usable material, were melted up; otherwise they came to rest, eventually, on some trash heap. And a great many objects that would be of tremendous interest to us now were deliberately and immediately destroyed—sometimes through careless indifference, sometimes through a religious fanaticism that considered anything pagan to be the work of the devil, as with the famous action of Bishop Landa of Mexico, who burned all of the books of the Mayas and Aztecs.

Systematic study of the people, organisms and environment of the tropics could not start until methods for such study had been worked out within the framework of Western culture itself, until such sciences as anthropology and biology had been developed. The European discovery of the non-European world was, of course, in itself a basic stimulus to the development of science. The bewildering variety of new kinds of plants, animals, things, people and customs called for some method whereby they could be named and catalogued, described and handled. The strange products of far lands helped men to look with new eyes at the familiar products of their own lands.

It was not until 1758 that a Swede, Carolus Linnaeus, devised a system whereby the plants and animals of all of the world could be given a uniform set of "scientific" names. It was not until about the same time that methods were worked out so that climatic factors like temperature 'could be measured with thermometers and the heat of Buitenzorg compared with that of Panama or London. Thus although Europe discovered the tropics at the end of the fifteenth century and started crude exploitation at once, scientific knowledge of the region developed very slowly.

There were, of course, good observers among the European explorers and colonists from the beginning. Of the Spaniards, we hear most about the *conquistadores,* but there were also people like Gonzalo Fernandez de Oviedo y Valdes who visited America several times and who was appointed official "historiographer" of the Indies in 1523. His *Natural History of the Indies* was published in Spanish, English and French versions in the sixteenth century, and was widely read. His famous contemporary, Bartolome de Las Casas, said the *History* "contained almost as many lies as pages," but it nevertheless remained the basic account of the marvels of tropical America for two hundred years.

The writings of Las Casas himself remained buried in the Spanish archives until 1855, when his *History of the Indies* was finally published, and most of the reports on America were similarly treated as secrets of the Spanish crown. In a comparable way, reports from the Asiatic tropics were apt to be treated as private documents of the great trading companies who had national monopolies.

Modern scientific societies started in the 17th century, the *Academia dei Lincei* in 1603, the Royal Society in 1660, the *Académie des sciences* in 1666, but these had little effect on tropical exploration or study until the next century. The expedition despatched by the French Academy to the region of Quito in 1735, to measure the length of a degree of the meridian in the neighborhood of the equator, might be called the first of the modern scientific expeditions in the tropics. Among the members was Charles Marie de La Condamine who, after the work at Quito was completed, carried out the first scientific exploration of the Amazon.

This was also the century of James Cook (1728–1779), the last of the great seafaring explorers, who opened to Europe the world of the central and south Pacific. Cook made a reputation as a mathematician and astronomer through his work as marine surveyor of Newfoundland and Labrador, and in 1768 he was given command of the bark *Endeavour,* which was outfitted by the Admiralty for observing the impending transit of Venus from Tahiti, and for pursuing geographical studies in the south Pacific. On this, and on his later trips with the *Resolution,* the *Adventure* and the *Discovery,* Cook added tremendously to Europe's knowledge of the Pacific tropics—and to England's claims to Empire. In 1778 he discovered for Europe the Hawaiian archipelago (which Spain had probably known about, but kept secret) and a year later (in February, 1779) he was killed there in an attempt to recover one of the *Discovery's* boats that had been stolen by the natives.

I called Cook the last of the great "seafaring" explorers, because after his time there were no more great land masses or archipelagos to be discovered, only cartographic details to be filled in. There was, however, still ample room for exploration of a specialized kind in the Arctic and Antarctic regions, and the continental interiors of Australia, Asia and Africa remained badly mapped and almost unknown to Europeans.

Interior Africa was protected from exploration and exploitation longer than any other continent, mostly, I think, by its indigenous diseases. The death rate among explorers and Europeans attempting settlement remained fantastic in the lowland tropical sections of the continent right up to the beginning of the present century; and the major features of the interior were unknown to Europeans until the latter half of the nineteenth century. The story of this final geographical exploration of Africa is very well known, partly because it occurred so recently, and partly because three of the explorers (David Livingstone, H. M. Stanley and Richard Burton) were also highly articulate, writing books that attracted wide attention.

There is still room for geographical exploration in some parts of Africa, along many of the tributaries of the Orinoco and Amazon river systems of South America, and among the rugged mountains of New Guinea. But these are details. The great days of exploration in the narrow, geographical sense, are over for the equatorial region. But exploration in the wide sense, of describing, understanding, and mastering the environment, has hardly begun.

Although hardly yet begun, this new type of exploration, this pushing ahead of the frontiers of knowledge in the equatorial regions, already has a long roster of distinguished names. An early example would be the Baron Alexander von Humboldt. He spent only five years (from 1799 to 1804) in the tropics, but he got material during these years for major contributions in several fields of scientific thought.

Humboldt's writings, among other things, provided reading material for young Charles Darwin when, in 1831, he set sail as naturalist on H.M.S. *Beagle*. Darwin also was five years on this voyage, gathering material which subsequently provided the impetus for his great theory of natural selection. And after Darwin begins the list that goes right down to our day—Alfred Russel Wallace, Henry Walter Bates, Richard Spruce, Thomas Belt, on to the earnest young scientists who can be found now working all the way around the globe from the laboratories of Barro Colorado in Panama to those of the Botanic Garden in Buitenzorg.

This, then, is a very brief sketch of the historical background of our Western knowledge of the tropics. It started with the explosive discovery in the years around 1500 that the seas of the world could be highways for the men of Europe who were searching for spices and gold and power. The ships and arms and political skill acquired during the previous centuries gave Western man the feeling that he was Lord of the Planet, master and arbiter of the lesser breeds that he encountered in his prowlings about the oceans. And, during the following centuries, he was able to maintain his position with the development of systems of nationalism, colonialism and economic exploitation until, in recent years, the non-Western world began to catch up with his techniques and ideas.

But from the beginning there has been another element in Western contact with the tropics. Along with the merchants, soldiers and politicians of the first wave of the Western explosion, there were men like Oviedo and Las Casas, interested in observing and understanding the new world that had been exposed by this blasting of the sea barriers. And the numbers of these men has slowly increased over the years, though they are still a tiny band when compared with the host of generals, diplomats and merchants that the West annually sends across the line of Cancer.

It is with the findings of this tiny band of observers that we shall be concerned in this book. And we might as well start out with their observations on the varieties of fellow men that they have encountered below the tropic.

CHAPTER III

★

The Varieties of Tropical Man

MAN is the commonest mammal on this planet, with something over two billion specimens crawling around on the planetary surface in the year 1950. 170,000 or so new specimens are born every day—which would be about 120 per minute. Something like 114,000 also die every day, but this still leaves a dizzy rate of increase. These figures are guesses, because for most of mankind no one has made a precise count; but they are based on a possible rate of 30 births and 20 deaths per year per thousand individuals, which is not unreasonable.

In some places, of course, field mice are more common than men. And a few kinds of rodents, the domestic mouse and the domestic rats, have achieved world populations of respectable size by adapting themselves to man's habits. Sometimes these domestic rats seem locally more abundant than men. But taking a world view, they fall far behind. To find animals with a scale of abundance really comparable with that of man, you have to look into things like codfish or grasshoppers or mosquitoes.

Man is by no means a peculiarly tropical animal—in fact, he is most common in Europe and China. All of the evidence indicates that he has long flourished in those latitudes despite the intemperate conditions. But he is widely distributed in the tropics, seems locally adapted to the varying conditions found within that climatic belt, and in some places (Java, for instance) he is extremely abundant.

Living men all belong to a single species which Linnaeus, who invented the system of scientific names for organisms, called Homo sapiens. Men form a single species because the criterion for "species" is breeding behavior: two kinds of animals, to be ranked as separate species, must have some barrier to interbreeding so that the two kinds, when mixed together under "normal" or "natural" conditions, retain their identity. The barrier to interbreeding may be of many kinds—arising from hybrid sterility, from behavior differences, from differences in the structure of the reproductive organs, and so forth.

With man, cultural barriers to interbreeding among the different varieties may be found, like the caste system of India or the color bar of the southern United States, but these barriers are sporadic and, in the long run, ineffectual. The only really effective barriers to human interbreeding—the sort of barriers that permitted the development of varieties among men in the first place—are geographical things like the Sahara desert and the Atlantic ocean.

There is a general agreement among zoologists that animal populations, however distinct in appearance, do not constitute "species" if kept separate by geographical factors only. Such populations are called "subspecies" unless or until physiological and behavior barriers arise to reenforce the geographical separation. Among birds and mammals we often have to guess whether two somewhat different forms in different places are "species" or "subspecies," since breeding experiments are generally difficult. But with man, modern transportation has arranged the experiments, and a glance at the obvious racial hybrids in a street crowd in Honolulu or Panama or, for that matter, New York, provides ample evidence of the ineffectiveness of interbreeding barriers, demonstrating that all living men are one species.

The geographical subspecies of man found in the tropics will be discussed later in this chapter; our concern now is with the human species as a whole. It is, among living animals, a rather isolated species, since the closest relatives are the great apes—the gorilla, the chimpanzee, the orang—which obviously differ from men in many ways. This situation is recognized by putting the human species "sapiens" in a genus, "Homo," by itself, and placing this genus in a family by itself, the "Hominidae." Actually, the great apes and man are similar enough in the structural points on which mammal classification is based (tooth structure, for instance) to put them all in a single family. But, as George Gaylord Simpson has pointed out, intelligence is perhaps as important as teeth in primate classification, and can best be recognized by keeping the great apes out of the human family. The apes (family Pongidae) and the men (family Hominidae) are grouped together into a single superfamily, the Hominoidea. This superfamily, along with others for the Old World and New World monkeys, form the suborder Anthropoidea; and the Anthropoidea, along with other suborders for the lemurs and the tarsiers, form the order Primates—of the class Mammalia of the vertebrate phylum of the animal kingdom.

Which puts man in his place.

The next question is, how did he get there?

A surprising number of fossils of men and man-like primates have been discovered, considering that these early humans were probably never very abundant animals. In Darwin's day there was much talk of the "missing link," but nowadays we have a superabundance of links—though they cannot be fitted into a chain on which all paleontologists will agree. The best known fossils are European: Heidelberg man, Piltdown man, Cro-Magnon man, Neanderthal man, and so forth. But this does not necessarily indicate that European conditions were important in human evolution; it may merely reflect the fact that many anthropologists and paleontologists live in Europe. I am not so much surprised at the number of fossils that have been found in Europe, as at the number that have been found in other places, considering how slight are the chances of discovery of such fossils in regions less well known scientifically. Of course it is significant that no fossils of man-like primates have been discovered in North America, where anthropologists and paleontologists are just as common as in Europe; this indicates that the main events in the evolution of man took place in the Old World. But where in the Old World, and under what climatic conditions, is something else.

Many fossil man-like primates have been found within the tropics of the Old World. First to be discovered, and one of the most interesting, is Pithecanthropus erectus of Java, discovered in 1891 by Eugene Dubois, a Dutch surgeon. Parts of other skulls of Pithecanthropus have since been found in Java, and these fragments have all been subject to minute scrutiny by many learned men who have reported their observations, disagreements and speculations at great length. The Java ape-man was more man than ape; he evidently was terrestrial, not arboreal; and it is believed that he possessed speech and made some use of tools. He probably lived in middle Pleistocene, a half a million or so years ago. Part of a child's skull was found in Java in 1936 in a lower Pleistocene deposit, two or three hundred thousand years older than the level of the adult Pithecanthropus material. If this "Modjokerto child" is of the same species as Pithecanthropus, which seems perfectly likely, the Java ape-man was busy with his subhuman occupations in the tropical forest for an unimaginable length of time, perhaps while his cousins somewhere on the mainland were about the business of evolving the details of structure of "true" or "modern" man.

Also from Java, but possibly much older, is a piece of jaw and three teeth from some man-like giant, similar to even bigger teeth that were found in an apothecary shop in southern China. It thus seems that nature "experimented" with giantism in the human stock in Pleistocene tropical Asia, but the giants apparently had no chance against their smaller cousins with the bigger brains.

Peking man (Sinanthropus) appears to have been contemporary with Java man, but considerably advanced toward the modern human type. Peking, of course, is way outside of the tropics, but a specimen that may be something like Sinanthropus was found in Tanganyika in 1935, and named Africanthropus. Other subhuman fossils (Australopithecus) have been found in South Africa, just outside of the tropics, thus making it seem probable that many different kinds of ape-men roamed through Africa and Asia in the early Pleistocene.

Fossils of true men, of Homo, have also been found in the tropics. Rhodesian man, for instance, found ninety feet deep in a zinc mine in northern Rhodesia, appears to be rather like the well-known Neanderthal man of Europe. A series of skulls of a similar man, called Homo soloensis, has been found in Java. This Solo man is definitely "retarded" in comparison with Neanderthal, and as Kroeber remarks, "looks like what we might conjecture Pithecanthropus to have evolved to on surviving in Java from middle to late Pleistocene."

All of this means little except that human and pre-human types have had a long geological history in the Asiatic and African tropics. But they have also had a long geological history in the region of Peking and around the Mediterranean, in times when the climate may or may not have had a tropical character. We learn nothing directly about the climatic circumstances under which man evolved. The significant changes may have occurred under semi-arid or cool conditions in higher latitudes, and been carried into the tropics; or they may have occurred in the rain forest, and pushed out to the north, advancing and retreating with the Pleistocene ice fronts.

A great deal more is known about the fossil cultures of man, about paleolithic and neolithic stone tools and Magdalenian cave paintings, than about the structure of the fossil men themselves, the characteristics of their species and races. But this detailed knowledge of fossil cultures concerns Europe, and especially the Mediterranean—our knowledge of fossil cultures in the tropics is limited to bits here and there that do not form sequences in any area and that are difficult to correlate with the carefully studied European sequences.

Living primates, except man, are almost purely tropical; the great apes are completely tropical, confined to equatorial rain forest country. Many human characteristics reflect the ape-like habits of our primate ancestors, but these ancestors surely got down out of the trees fairly early in the process of evolving toward man. I also suspect that they got out of the forest, mostly because life in the forest would be too easy, would hardly present the "challenge" necessary for the development of human intelligence.

The tropical rain forest men today represent the least progressive human stocks—bushmen, pygmies, Amazonian Indians. It is as though they had been "pushed" into this environment by the competition of the more progressive stocks. A comparable phenomenon can be seen in the geographical relations of organisms (including man) whereby the least progressive stocks get "pushed" to the periphery—in the case of man, to Australia, Tasmania and Tierra del Fuego.

It seems to me likely, in short, that human evolution, taking place on the Asiatic and African continents, involved venturing out from the forests into the savannah country. These early men, forming into "packs" and developing speed at running and cunning in tribal organization, could thus exploit the almost limitless food supply offered by the herds of grazing mammals. Pack formation is surely at the base of much of our instinctive equipment, as has been persuasively argued by Trotter and Carveth Read; and many of our physical adaptations are for running in open country rather than for slipping through the forest.

Such developments would most likely take place in the sub-equatorial trade wind belt, where the wet forest conditions gradually give way to the semiarid grasslands. Such a belt has probably always existed on either side of the equatorial forest region, because of the general nature of atmospheric circulation on our planet, though the exact location of the belt has varied with the changing geological climates of our past.

Our hairless condition, if nothing else, makes it seem likely that this early evolution involved tropical or subtropical grasslands, rather than regions of contrasting seasons at high latitudes. Surely, under glacial climatic conditions, we would have developed a woolly covering or some sort of physical adaptation to winter conditions. Of course, once the "human level" of intelligence had been reached, northern environments became open to man through cultural adaptation—skin coverings and fire—and the conquest of such physically unfavorable environments may have offered further challenge for the continued development of intelligence and cultural adaptations. But in the beginning man surely was a product of a "genial" rather than a "glacial" climate, and a large part of the human stock may always have lived under the "genial" conditions of the tropics.

The discovery of subhuman fossils from such diverse places as Europe, Africa, China and Java, and of clearly human fossils from even more widely separated regions (including Australia), proves that men and man-like primates have had a very wide geographical distribution for a very long time. Only in America is the antiquity of man doubtful. No subhuman fossils have been found in the New World nor, for that matter, any fossils of apes, though true man has probably been in America for quite a while, since clear evidence of human activity has been found in deposits of Pleistocene age.

This very wide and very ancient human distribution provides a basis for geographical variation. Many organisms vary geographically and such variation has been intensively studied in animals like mammals, birds and butterflies, because it seems to offer a basis for the origin of species. When breeding populations of organisms become wholly or partially isolated by barriers, such as mountains, seas or deserts, evolution in each isolated population may assume a separate course, new variations or mutations spreading only within the geographically limited, inter-breeding population. If this process goes far enough, a particular population may become so different from its fellows that even if the geographical barriers become ineffective, mixture will not occur. The populations have reached the stage of being "distinct species."

The human tendency to wander and to mate with any other man-like animal encountered, would serve to counteract the biological tendency toward geographical variation. If man were less ingenious in getting across seas, mountains and deserts, and less inclined to sexual promiscuity, he might have developed into very distinct varieties on, say, each island of the East Indies, as has happened with most birds and butterflies. As it is, specimens of indigenous man from Australia, Japan, Scandinavia, South Africa and South America look very different, demonstrating that geographical variation has been operating. But if male and female specimens from such diverse places are caged together, mating occurs without difficulty, because neither the reproduc-tive organs nor the patterns of instinctive behavior are greatly modified; and the resulting offspring turn out to be perfectly vigorous and fertile, showing a blending of the superficial distinc-tive characteristics of the parent stocks.

These two conflicting tendencies—toward the formation of geographical varieties and toward the intermixture of all human stocks—produce a result that, from the point of view of an orderly classifier, can only be called a mess. The whole subject is, of course, further confused by the fact that the classifiers themselves are men who must fit somehow or other into their own classifications. This might not matter, except that the subject of human classification has got involved with the question of whether this human variety is "superior" to that one, "better," "more intelligent," "more backward" or something of that sort.

I have spent a great deal of time studying geographical variation in butterflies and mosquitoes, but I have never got involved in any discussion as to whether a subspecies of butterfly in Cuba, for instance, was "better" than a subspecies in Haiti. Yet with the varieties of man it seems impossible to get away from what the sociologists call "value judgments."

Anthropologists of one school, trying to do away with "race prejudice," sound as though they were arguing that there is no such thing as "race." They admit (grudgingly) that a Scandinavian and an Australian blackfellow look rather different, but point out that a whole series of transition types can easily be found; and that if these transitions were all lined up in a row, it would be impossible to tell where the Scandinavian ended and the blackfellow began. No one can quarrel with this statement, because it is put in the subjunctive, *if* the transitions *were* all lined up in a row. But working with the present indicative, with actual fact, we find the transitions scattered all over the map, each one waiting to be studied in its geographical context.

I suspect that in the end, what with the promiscuity of the wandering Scandinavians and the low cultural resistance of the blackfellows, human races will disappear. But in the meanwhile, we can study what remnants of geographical pattern remain and we need some verbal framework on which to hang these studies, some classification of racial types, of human varieties. There is a large collection of schemes among which to choose.

The modern science of animal classification stems from a book published by Carolus Linnaeus in 1758, called the *Systema Naturae,* the "system of nature." He starts the book with Homo sapiens and I think his division of the species into four varieties (and a few monstrosities) has been little improved. He recognized:

Americanus: rufus, cholericus, rectus. (red, irascible, upright.)
Europaeus: albus, sanguineus, torosus. (white, bloodthirsty, brawny.)
Asiaticus: luridus, melancholicus, rigidus. (yellow, sad, unbending.)
Afer: niger, phlegmaticus, laxus. (black, calm, lazy.)

My translations are, of course, rather free. Linnaeus surely meant *sanguineus,* in the sense of the medieval classification of temperaments, as "hopeful"; but the older Latin sense of "bloodthirsty" strikes me as more appropriate. This Linnaean classification is clearly arbitrary and inadequate—but so are the dozens of classifications that have been proposed since.

Even the racial names are silly: white, red, yellow, brown and black. Only brown and (sometimes) black are reasonably descriptive. The North American word "paleface" is rather more apt than "white," and it might be useful to start a movement for the substitution. I don't know what to do about "red" and "yellow." The geographical names are as bad as the color terms. Names like "Mongolian" and "Caucasian" involve spreading a hypothetical place of origin over a lot of additional territory. "Indian" is always causing trouble. Some anthropologists try to avoid ambiguity by condensing "American Indian" into "Amerind," but this always looks to me as though it might be a label for a variety of grapefruit.

A few anthropologists achieve a neutral effect by translating the color terms into Greek. By this scheme we would have "melanoderms" (black skins), "leucoderms" (white skins), "xanthoderms" (yellow skins) and so forth. There seems a clear advantage in this, since most people would be impressed by the learned sound of the Greek words without worrying too much about the literal meanings. Such big words might even prove useful in the war on race prejudice. "Leucoderm superiority," for instance, has a diseased sound, though the meaning is exactly the same as "white superiority." Politicians in South Africa or the

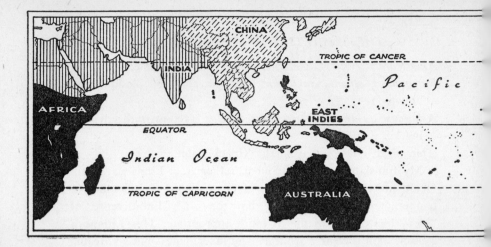

southern United States who depend on waving the banner of white superiority and racial prejudice might, with this system, be accused of spreading "leucodermosis."

But the problem of classification and terminology is secondary in this book. Our present interest is in attempting a sketch of the racial diversity of indigenous man in the tropics. I say "indigenous" because for the moment we'll ignore the paleface intruders from Europe, ubiquitous though they are. Perhaps geography will furnish the best frame for this sketch, with the discussion centered on the different tropical continental areas.

America. The earlier anthropologists mostly regarded the "Red Indians" as a separate major race, but recent students generally class them as a subgroup of the "Mongoloids." Within the area, there is considerable diversity in physique, from the Eskimos to the Fuegians, though the diversity is perhaps less than in comparable Old World areas. Present differences may reflect various waves of migration of rather divergent racial stocks into America in Late Pleistocene and post-Pleistocene times.

The inhabitants of tropical America in pre-Columbian days presented a tremendous diversity in cultural development. There was a whole gamut of cultural types, from the food-gathering

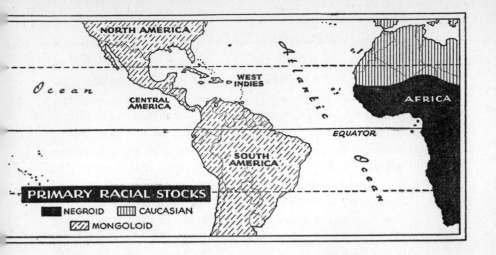

PRIMARY RACIAL STOCKS
- NEGROID
- CAUCASIAN
- MONGOLOID

tribes of the Amazonian forests to the complex civilizations of the Aztecs, Mayas and Incas. These cultures were mostly shattered by the post-Columbian impact of Western civilization. The people and cultures of the West Indies disappeared completely and promptly, those of the coastal mainland only a little more slowly. The mountain people showed a surprising cultural and physical resistance; their leaders and their political systems gave way, but their daily ways of life changed only slowly. The forest peoples were affected least of all, and some of these, like the Motilones of Colombia, remain today completely untouched by the events that have remade the rest of tropical America. These people, unfortunately, are as resistant to anthropologists as they are to politicians and militarists, so that we know very little about them.

Africa. At first thought, tropical Africa might seem as uniform, racially, as pre-Colombian tropical America—the one being full of Negroes and the other of Indians. The Africans, however, are much more obviously physically diverse than the Americans, ranging from the very tall, slender people of the White Nile to the Congo pygmies and the steatopygous Hottentots. They have been extensively bled, measured and photographed by anthropologists, so that data on physique are abundant.

Curiously, the tropical Africans are more uniform culturally than the tropical Americans. An anthropologist might deny this, since the Africans show endless variety in items like language, kinship rules, burial customs ånd other things dear to the anthropological heart. But these, it seems to me, are all variations on at most two themes, food-gathering and agriculture. This matter of cultures really belongs to the next chapter, but I can't resist pointing out here the absence of anything corresponding to the cultural level of civilization in tropical Africa. Civilization, of course, is a matter of definition; but however defined, it is clear enough that there has been nothing in tropical Africa comparable with the Aztec and Incan empires or the Mayan city states or the elaborate cultures of tropical Asia.

The search for the reason for this may help us in understanding the causes of civilization—a matter that seems always to interest us tremendously in our precariously civilized existence. I cannot believe that it has anything to do with "race"—otherwise why wouldn't civilization be far more likely among the diverse African types than among the uniform Americans? Any "inferiority of the negro" argument does not work. A Congo savage may seem a genius when compared with a tropical American Indian. The answer, of course, may be that the African has too much sense to be civilized. Or perhaps it has something to do with the configuration of the mountain ranges on the two continents. Or perhaps it is a matter of the accidents of history and pre-history. I have no theory to sell, only a general distrust of all of the theories that I know; and one of the reasons for this distrust is that I fail to see how the theories distinguish between the actual course of human development in tropical Africa and tropical America.

Asia. The Tropic of Cancer, in crossing Asia, cuts off many fabled lands: peninsular India, Burma, Siam, Cambodia, Java, Malaya. Within those limits, we have almost every known racial type of man, almost every known basic type of culture. We talk about the melting pot of the United States, but the ingredients that have been thrown into our country seem limited indeed when compared with the materials in the Asiatic brew.

Since we have the evidence of Pithecanthropus in the south and Sinanthropus in the north, we can assume that tropical Asia has been inhabited ever since there was any animal that could be called human. If man didn't originate in this area, he must have moved in very soon after originating somewhere else; and new types, as soon as they became distinct, must have continued to move in, mixing with such of their predecessors as weren't killed off.

This is particularly true of tropical India, where this Asiatic brew is stickiest of all. Baron Meston, in the *Encyclopaedia Britannica* article on India, recognizes eight racial types among contemporary Indians. He supposes that in remote antiquity, India was occupied by a negroid people, that later the "Dravidian" races entered through Baluchistan from western Asia, followed by Mongoloid peoples from the northeast, and then by the long series of invasions in more or less historic times through the northwest passes of "Aryans" and so forth.

The basic racial type of Burma, Indo-China, Siam and the East Indies is something called "Malay" or "Indonesian," or in Hooton's terminology "Indonesian-Mongoloid." Speculation as to the racial elements entering into the make-up of this blend can be almost unlimited, since the mixing has been thorough. There is a general agreement, however, that the result is one of the pleasantest human types, from almost any point of view.

The history of culture in tropical Asia is as tangled as the history of race. Northwest India, just outside of the tropics, is one of the possible "cradles" of civilization, with city-states in Sindh and the Punjab contemporary with the civilizations of the Nile and the Tigris-Euphrates area. There has been ample time, then, for all of the civilizations of the Old World to bring their influence to bear on the tropical peoples. Yet through all of this stretch of history, some of the forest peoples have persisted at the most primitive, Stone Age, food-gathering stage of culture.

Oceania. The islands of the Pacific have long been the happy hunting ground of anthropologists—pleasant islands, inhabited by delightful people with charming customs. (Head-hunting and cannibalism, from this point of view, serve merely to add variety to the custom collection.) The region also provides beautiful material for racial study in the Polynesian-Melanesian contrasts. In Hooton's classification, the Polynesians are listed as a "composite race, predominantly white" with a Mongoloid and Melanesian-Papuan mixture. The Melanesians, on the other hand, are a "composite race, predominantly negroid" which he considers to be composed of "Negrito plus Australoid plus convex-nosed Mediterranean plus minor fractions of Malay and Polynesian."

It seems probable that the Polynesians achieved more or less their present racial blend somewhere in Asia, and peopled the Pacific Islands in successive waves of migration out from this homeland. It is likely that this was a fairly recent phenomenon, and parts of the process are documented by legends that have an almost historical force. The Melanesians, on the other hand, probably represent a stock with a long history on the nearer islands.

The *Kon-Tiki* story, so persuasively told by Thor Heyerdahl, has given wide currency to his theory that the Polynesians represent a pre-Inca people who migrated from America. Certainly Heyerdahl has given a convincing demonstration that it is perfectly possible to go from Peru to the South Seas in a balsa raft such as the Incas used, thus making it seem more likely that there were such contacts in ancient times. Anthropologists still feel, however, that the evidence for the Asiatic origin of the Polynesian race and for most elements of Polynesian culture is overwhelming. Our knowledge about the peoples and cultures of these fascinating islands has been admirably summarized in a recent book by Douglas Oliver, *The Pacific Islands,* which should

be consulted by anyone interested in reading about this region.
Australia. An outsider, reading anthropological textbooks, gets the idea that two physical anthropologists rarely show complete agreement on any question of racial classification. The Australians and Tasmanians provide the exception, since everyone seems to agree that they represent the most "primitive" of surviving human stocks—with reference both to physique and culture. The Tasmanians need not concern us, since they lived well to the south of the tropics and anyway became extinct in 1879. But the Australian blackfellows are still struggling along in the Australian tropics, and consequently provide proper material for this book.

The anthropologists agree that the blackfellows are primitive; but they are far from agreeing about where to place them in the racial schemes of classification. Hooton's system appeals to me most: he places the Australian blackfellows as "predominantly White," representing the archaic stock from which the present palefaces are descended. They would thus be rather distant cousins of the hairy Ainus of Japan, who are more generally classed as "White."

It seems, at any rate, very probable that the Australian blackfellows have no connection with the African Negroes, except for some intermixture from the Papuans of New Guinea, who probably do belong to a primary Negro race. Thus whether these blackfellows are really "White" or not, they at least demonstrate the absurdity of skin color as a primary basis for the classification of human varieties. Color is certainly convenient, but after all it is only skin-deep.

All of this adds up to a very inadequate and possibly misleading sketch of the tropical varieties of man. My object has been to show that almost the whole known range of human racial variation is found in some part or another of this tropical zone, a range that would be increased beyond what I have listed here if the post-Columbian migrations had been included.

In reading about these racial classifications and physical studies, I am impressed more than anything else by our ignorance. We know a great deal about the proportions of the skull, about the shape of the nose, about stature, even about blood groups, among these various people. But we seem to know extraordinarily little about possible differences in physiology, and even less about possible differences in mental development.

These varieties do differ in skin color, in hair texture, and in skull shape; and it seems likely that there would also be variation in climatic adaptation, perhaps in nutritional requirements, and in psychological elements like temperament. Not that this would add up to one variety being "better" than another in any absolute sense; but that one race might be found to be better adapted to a particular environmental situation than another. The data on this point, however, seem to be very scanty indeed.

One difficulty is that the physical and psychological make-up of man is overwhelmed by an independent variable, culture. At least culture seems to behave in some respects as though it were independent of the physical man, just as it sometimes behaves as though it were independent of the climatic environment. But culture is such an important element in any study of man's environmental relationships that it seems best to devote a separate chapter to its analysis.

CHAPTER IV

★

The Varieties of Tropical Culture

AN is an animal, all right. If a specimen is cut open, stomach, lungs, intestines and such like organs are found, differing only in detail from the comparable organs of apes and monkeys. Even the brain, of which man is so proud, doesn't look very peculiar if it is examined pickled in a jar of alcohol. Functions as well as structures seem about the same in man and in his primate cousins. Men and monkeys equally need air, equally depend on a continuing supply of food, equally dispose of body wastes by a periodic dumping of liquid and solid material, equally maintain their kind by an odd sort of behavior through which two slightly different individuals get involved with something called sex.

Yet, undeniably, man differs in profound and significant ways from all of the other animals with which he shares the planet. To check our random list of functions again—breathing in man and other animals is about the same, but look at what man does to his food, and at the behavior that surrounds the eating of it; look at the problems associated with urination and defecation (in some cultures, at least); look at the taboos, morals, rituals, fears and pleasures that have got attached to sex. Reproduction, excretion, digestion, were never this complicated for any monkey or any guinea pig.

47

These peculiarities of man, these ways in which he differs so strikingly from all other organisms, are covered by the anthropological concept of "culture." This, clearly, is different from the kind of culture claimed by Boston or dispensed by finishing schools along the Hudson. Anthropological culture isn't exclusive to any class or place—it is a common character of all living men, of Hottentots and Australian blackfellows, as well as Parisians, Brahmins and Mandarins. The culture of different peoples may be different; but all people have it.

This basic "culture concept" of modern anthropology is the subject of many books and endless discussion. Clyde Kluckhohn's definition, in *Mirror for Man,* is as good as any: "the total way of life of a people, the social legacy the individual acquires from his group . . . that part of the environment that is the creation of man."

The inheritance of culture depends on language. Language—a system of symbols for conveying ideas—is the peculiar invention of man, differing abruptly and basically from the corresponding animal cries of alarm and pleasure. To be sure language sometimes seems not too different from the conversational cluckings of hens, the mimicking song of mocking birds or the mating signals of crickets. But these, at most, are analogues, counterparts of functions peripheral to the main function of language, which is the transmission of thought. I don't know whether any non-human animal "thinks" or not, but I am sure that none has a word-symbol system for conveying thoughts. Mother cats may be able to teach their kittens to hunt, mother birds their fledglings to fly; and the things that a human infant learns in the first few months may hardly differ from this non-human learning. But with the development of words, of sound mimicry, and of sound-thing association, a whole new kind of learning, purely human, becomes possible. Memory and oral tradition make this learning cumulative, allowing it to increase, change, diversify over generations. The invention of writing multiplies the possibility of accumulation enormously, enabling simple "culture" to become transformed into complex "civilization."

From the point of view of inheritance, then, culture could be treated as the sum of all of the customs, information, attitudes, habits and so forth that depend for transmission on the various mechanisms associated with language. Each of us, every man, has a double inheritance: one biological, determining the shape of his nose, the color of his skin, and perhaps his mental aptitudes; the other cultural, determining his way of life. It is the second inheritance that, for better or for worse, distinguishes man from the beasts.

Culture can be (and has been) studied as a thing-in-itself, quite apart from the human animal that created it. Thus the evolution of a particular culture trait can be studied—the wearing of pants, the treatment of mothers-in-law, the ornamenting of baskets—and each such trait may be found to have some particular place of origin, a characteristic pattern of spread or diffusion, a history of modification leading perhaps to ever greater development and wider use, or perhaps to extinction. Anthropologists study cultural conflict and cultural hybridization; they dissect particular cultures into basic components and work out the functions of cultural components the way physiologists work out the functions of bodily organs.

In contrast with the point of view that regards culture as a thing-in-itself is the point of view that regards different human cultural traits as products of different human racial characteristics. This is called "racial determinism." It has long since been abandoned by anthropologists, and I cannot think of any serious examples—though the proponents of the Aryan nonsense of Hitler's Germany were serious enough in their contemporary effect. "Acquisitive" Jews, "bloodthirsty" Indians, "traitorous" Japs, "happy-go-lucky" Negroes exemplify the sort of thing I mean by "racial determinism."

Still a third point of view toward culture can be recognized, that of "environmental determinism," according to which the type of culture and the extent of its development depend on the physical environment—on temperature, rainfall, topography, and so forth. The "climate and civilization" people represent the extreme of environmental determinism in this sense.

There is probably some element of truth in all three of these points of view. Culture surely is based in the physical nature of man—in the organs that make speech possible, and in the intelligence that makes speech useful. And the early direction of cultural development may well have varied with the varying physical characteristics of earliest man, though here we are on purely speculative ground. This would be racial determinism. Once started, the development of culture types has surely depended greatly on environmental circumstances—on, for instance, the kinds of food available, on the availability of materials for tools, on the climatic and topographic hazards and advantages. Obviously the climate has helped mould Eskimo culture; may it not, then, have also moulded the culture of the Greeks? This would allow an element of environmental determinism. And once a total culture, or a single cultural trait, has started development, truly it often continues as if it were independent of the originating men or the controlling environment, behaving as a thing-in-itself.

In this book we are interested in seeing what kinds of culture man has developed in the tropics. This turns out to be a fairly large order, since practically every known major variety of culture has been found at some time, somewhere, in the tropics. About all that can be done, then, is to try to illustrate this cultural diversity.

We commonly divide cultures into two major classes, "primitive" and "civilized." This turns out to be pretty arbitrary. The difference is clear enough when members of a complex society come in contact with members of a relatively simple society, as when European explorers meet Australian blackfellows. But if we start out and try to sort all known human cultures into two piles, one labelled "primitive" and the other "civilized," we soon get into difficulties. Obviously the clearly civilized societies have evolved gradually from primitive origins, so that the concepts of primitive and civilized are not contrasts, but parts of a continuous spectrum. The boundaries of such regional divisions in a continuum must be determined by some arbitrary process of definition.

There are further complications, because existing cultures cannot really be arranged in any lineal series from simple to complex—there are different kinds of simplicity and complexity. Furthermore we cannot assume that living, simple cultures are comparable with the extinct, historical cultures that were ancestral to our present civilizations.

Yet, if we are to study cultures and to write about them, we have to have some verbal frame on which to hang our observations and ideas. This involves the creation of some system of categories, the classification of known cultures into some named series of varieties. Since we are making divisions in a continuum, the divisions are bound to be artificial, arbitrary, man-made—not "natural." But the divisions may none-the-less be useful, particularly if we try always to keep in mind their arbitrary basis in convenience.

The most convenient distinguishing mark of civilization is writing, the development of a system of recording language, so that the accumulation and transmission of knowledge is freed from complete dependence on man's fallible memory. Civilizations would thus be the "literate" cultures; and the uncivilized or primitive cultures would be "non-literate"—a word that hasn't yet become overloaded with objectionable connotations. We will do well to start our tropical survey with these non-literate cultures, leaving any detailed inquiry into the nature of tropical civilizations for a subsequent chapter.

There are, of course, a great many different non-literate cultures known to anthropologists, and some method of further subdivision is needed. The commonest system of classification is according to basic economy, by which we have the food-gatherers, the hunters, the herders, and the gardeners or agriculturists.

The food-gatherers, with no domestic animals (except the dog), with no cultivated plants, with no fixed places of abode, are generally considered the most primitive of surviving cultures. All of mankind must have remained in the food-gathering stage during most of the course of cultural evolution, until some culture, or perhaps several cultures, took the first steps toward the domestication of plants and animals back in the Neolithic.

How and why these first steps toward agriculture were taken we shall never know—which leaves a splendid field for speculation. The process was certainly slow and irregular. It seems likely that our savage ancestors were far from regarding agriculture as an unmixed blessing, since it soon involved such unpleasant features as regular habits and hard work. Agriculture is an insidious business, though. Once developed or adopted, it enables many more people to live on a given area of land, and human breeding habits being what they are, this population increase soon appears. The tribe is then saddled with agriculture for all eternity, since the old ways cannot yield enough food for the new numbers.

A few food-gathering peoples resort to agriculture in emergencies, when driven to such drastic action by prolonged scarcity of game. This shows that such people could be agricultural if they wanted to—but they avoid the necessity by desisting from agriculture as soon as game conditions return to normal and before their own population has made any untoward gain. Some of the Plains Indians of North America were enabled, by a lucky fluke, to escape the agricultural treadmill: they took to the horse, when this appeared as a result of the Spanish intrusion, and when they discovered that their population could be maintained by this more efficient method of hunting, agriculture was abandoned forthwith.

A few peoples apparently have never taken up with any of these insidious methods of food-producing: we find them living today in a food-gathering culture that seems not unlike the culture that probably characterized all of mankind fifteen or twenty thousand years ago. We call such people "backward"— but maybe they are the cleverest of all in having managed to avoid, through all of these millenia, those first fatal steps toward the primrose-lined, ambition-greased, chute of civilization.

Such are the Negrito peoples of the heavy forests of many parts of tropical Asia—the Semang of Malaya, the Aeta of the Philippines, the Kubu of Sumatra, and the Toala of Celebes. The Semang of the Malayan forests, described by Daryll Forde, may serve as an example of all of these. A band of twenty or thirty individuals will have a "territory" of some twenty square miles of forest, over which they wander, collecting what they can find that is edible: berries, nuts, pith, leaves, grubs, roots. The greatest feasts are when the durians are ripe, and particular durian trees are considered to be the "property" of individuals, though the fruit is shared with the group. Hunting and fishing are sporadic, depending on need and opportunity; rats, squirrels, birds and lizards form the usual game, and the big animals are feared and avoided. The Semang use a bow, with arrows treated with vegetable poisons, which they are expert in preparing; and they devise various sorts of snares and traps.

They make crude, temporary shelters of rattan; clothes are limited to girdles and necklaces, which are regarded as magic charms. Their chief tools are made of bamboo, that most useful of tropical plants.

The Malayan forests are inhabited by another group of food-gatherers, the Sakai, who may be of the same general racial stock as the Australians, and thus quite different from the Negritos. Their culture is more elaborate than that of the Semangs: they build huts on stilts, to which they return fairly regularly, and they use the blowpipe in hunting.

These Semangs and Sakais are in contact with each other and with the "savage" Malays (who are in a food-producing stage of culture); yet there is notably little interchange of cultural items, and no tendency on the part of the forest people to take up "progress" in any of its forms. Of course, the contacts of any particular individual are very limited. As Forde has pointed out: "It is difficult to realize the narrow bounds within which the life of an individual is passed. Throughout his life a man will remain with a handful of his kin. From time to time he will encounter for a few days other groups of similar size. Very rarely will he go far afield, and few strangers cross his path. The knowledge and opinions of his elder relatives are the only views he hears. This limited range of contact and stimulus is of fundamental importance in understanding the stability and slowness of change among the simpler societies of man."

Most of the peoples of tropical Africa, of course, are food-producers; but there are food-gatherers, the much-discussed pygmies, in many areas of equatorial forest. In tropical America, though, there seem to have been no exclusively food-gathering people within historic times. The Indians of the Amazon and Orinoco are primitive enough by most standards, but they all have got involved to some degree in growing plants in the clearings that they make in the forests.

Careful study of the habits of these very primitive food-producers, combined with a study of the characteristics of the kind of plants that were domesticated, offers about the only factual basis on which to build theories about the origin of agriculture. The building of such theories may seem a particularly futile waste of time, a fine example of sterile scholarship. But I don't think so. Surely man has no more important problem than that of gaining understanding of himself. And the understanding of his present condition and present nature will surely in part depend on an understanding of the historical processes through which he arrived at this present state. With a problem like the origin of agriculture, which occurred before the advent of historical records, any clear proof or complete certainty will probably always be impossible. But the weighing of relative probabilities, the search for the traces of indirect evidence that may be found in archeology, ethnology and botany, will be no less helpful in contributing to this understanding of what we are and how we got that way.

In the last chapter, I went over some of the evidence pointing to the probability that man, as a zoological species, had a tropical origin. Now I want to show the probability that agriculture, basic to the cultural development of modern, civilized man, similarly had a tropical origin.

A great many anthropologists, botanists and agriculturists have come to suspect that the first cultivated plants were root crops, vegetatively propagated, like yams, sweet potatoes and cassava. This idea seems at first rather startling, because we are accustomed to associating the origin of plant cultivation with the origin of the basic cereals, of wheat, barley, rice and maize. The great civilizations, certainly, have always been based on some form of cereal cultivation, but this is far from proving that the idea of plant cultivation arose in connection with the cereals. The most primitive forms of cultivation, in fact, seem to be associated with quite different sorts of plants.

Food-gatherers, like the Semang of Malaya, depend greatly on edible roots and tubers. As E. J. Payne long ago pointed out, "the act of planting a root . . . scarcely differs from that of digging one up; and the familiar 'woman stick' of digger tribes, a simple pointed and fire-hardened stake, is also the general implement of primitive agriculture. So easy is the transition that the manioc (cassava), the most valuable among the roots, is even yet in rich soils cultivated by merely dropping a piece of the stalk into the hole from which the mature root has been extracted; one digging operation thus suffices for gathering the old crop and planting a new one."

One of the root-crops, yams, was found in the tropics of both hemispheres, cultivated by American Indians, by Polynesians, and by many other people long before their "discovery" by Europeans. Is this, then, the basic cultivated plant, the point of origin of all agriculture?

Any discussion of this—or, indeed, any discussion of the origin of agriculture—gets us very soon involved with the question of whether plant cultivation was a single discovery, made only once in human cultural development; or whether it has been made repeatedly, in many places, at many times; or whether it has been made at most twice, once in the Old World and once in the New. This, of course, is no peculiar problem of agriculture. It arises constantly in the study of man's development. The same questions can be asked of language, of the use of fire, of tools, of writing, of the whole complex of "civilization." We may never find a decisive answer and the formation of any judgment is difficult.

We can perhaps make progress most readily by focussing on a single question: whether agriculture in the Old World and the New arose independently. This surely is related to another question of general interest, whether civilization arose independently in the two hemispheres.

The question, in this simple form, is still far from easy and the answer is far from clear. Scientists are apt to feel strongly about the matter, though, dividing sharply into the separatist school, considering American agriculture and American civilization to be independent inventions; and the diffusionist school, tracing all sorts of relationships between the two hemispheres. I find myself in a curious situation in this regard, because I long subscribed wholeheartedly to the theory of American independence, ridiculing the fellows who found similarities between Mayan and Egyptian pyramids or hieroglyphics, and nodding in sage agree-

ment with the remark that there are only a few shapes practical
for a pot, so that it is no very remarkable coincidence that these
few shapes should have been hit upon by various people at
various times.

I still raise my eyebrows at suggestions involving the Mayas
with lost tribes of Israel, or at any relation of the empire of Peru
to the empire of China through some lost Pacific continent of
Mu. But my faith in American independence has been shaken by
a whole series of trivialities like those yams (and gourds and
cotton) and by the undeniable seafaring ability of many preliterate people like the Polynesians. We know that the Polynesians reached all of the remote islands of the Pacific, which
opens the possibility that other people before them may have
moved across the Pacific, carrying the idea of agriculture, and
perhaps carrying seeds or other propagating material. Such an
interchange, if it occurred, must have been at a very early period,
however, because the list of plants common to Old and New
World agriculture is small indeed when compared with the lists
of plants that were not shared by the two hemispheres before
the time of European contacts.

The idea of plant cultivation is certainly very ancient, whether
it was acquired only once in human history, or whether (as
seems more likely) several different cultures in different parts of
the world adopted cultivation independently. And a very great
many different kinds of plants were cultivated at an early stage
in man's cultural history. In fact, man has not domesticated any
basic food-plant within historic times—though he has moved
many food-plants all over the map. The cultivation of plants for
medicinal or magical purposes is also very ancient—perhaps as
old as cultivation for food, or perhaps older, since primitive man
seems often to have carried out sensible ideas for magical
reasons.

A great deal of effort has gone into the search for the wild
ancestors of the various kinds of cultivated plants, but the sub-

ject still remains curiously obscure. In some cases, like that of the American corn, maize, we simply have no idea what the ancestral wild plant may have been. In other cases, several possible ancestors have been found, and authorities debate as to which wild species may have been most important, or whether the domestic plant may be a hybrid of several wild kinds. In some ways it looks as though the plants that early man cultivated may have been sorts that were then on the verge of extinction, things ill adapted to the competition of the wild. The weeds that plague our gardens so are like this—without man to clear the ground for them, they become the rarest of plants, growing only in precarious, temporary situations like river sand bars. Maybe some of the food-plants started as weeds, volunteers around the camp sites.

It should be clear enough, then, that discussion of the origin of cultivated plants is of the nature of more or less intelligent guessing. But it does seem that the numerous kinds of cultivated plants can be derived from a few centers of origin: Central America (Guatemala and southern Mexico); the eastern slopes of the South American Andes; the Asiatic tropics; the African tropics; and the Near East. All of these except the last are tropical, and the exception is not far out of the tropics. Of the three cereals on which man has built his great civilizations (maize, rice and wheat), two are surely of tropical origin and the third (wheat) may well include elements from the highlands of tropical Abyssinia.

Agriculture had already progressed to a considerable degree of complexity at the "dawn of history" in the Mediterranean and Asiatic civilizations, and the exact nature of this progress, from digging stick to hoe to plow, can only be guessed. The progress toward complexity certainly varied greatly according to local conditions, which made irrigation necessary in one place, measures to prevent erosion necessary in another, measures to reenforce soil fertility necessary in a third, and so forth.

This diversity makes any generalization hazardous. Nevertheless it can well be said that agriculture, given time enough, passes through three periods: "a period of 'exploitation' during which the virgin soil is literally mined of its fertility, a period of 'conservation' during which efforts are made to stem the growing losses of fertility from cropping and erosion, and a period of 'reconstruction' during which the soil may actually be built up and improved. In the United States, we are only now beginning to enter the second stage. Europe has entered the third only within the past few centuries; and crop yields in certain regions of Europe are now higher than they were when America was discovered. But the ancient Peruvians were practising an advanced type of agriculture long before the conquest. Their terrace agriculture was so old that at the time of the arrival of the first Europeans they knew nothing of its origin, ascribed it to the gods, and considered it to be coeval with the world itself." (Quoting from Mangelsdorf and Reeves.) The type of agriculture practised by any particular culture is, then, more a reflection of the environment than of the age and total complexity of the culture. As Mangelsdorf and Reeves point out, "no people have ever passed beyond the exploitative stage of agriculture voluntarily; they have always been forced into making the change."

In general, however, the more elaborate systems of agriculture, involving irrigation, tillage, and great diversity of crops, characterize the very complex cultures that we call civilizations. The cultivation of preliterate cultures is mostly a much more simple affair, of digger stick, hoe, and fields that are abandoned after one or two crops.

The origin of animal domestication is as mysterious as that of plant cultivation, except that there are fewer kinds of animals to be accounted for. Anthropologists once thought that animal domestication preceded plant cultivation, and they made a sequence from food-gathering to animal-hunting to animal-herding to the cultivation of plants. It now seems probable, though, that plants were tamed first—except, of course, for the dog, which probably tamed itself.

Only two of the common domestic animals are clearly tropical —pigs and chickens—and the first steps toward animal domestication may well have been taken by peoples living to the north of the tropics. Donkeys, horses, sheep, goats, camels and perhaps cattle seem to have developed from wild ancestors characteristic of the grasslands and arid country north of the tropic, and pastoral cultures today hardly exist in the tropics outside of Africa. The extensive grasslands of tropical Africa have permitted the development of several culture varieties based on cattle, but these cattle seem to be more important as signs of wealth or prestige than as sources of food, so that the cattle-raising tribes either also cultivate, or else resort to raiding and warfare as a supplement to the cattle economy.

Pastoral people generally seem to be war-like, which may reflect the development of animal-breeding from animal-hunting, and the relation of animal-hunting to man-hunting. Certainly herding, as among these African tribes, is generally a manly affair; while cultivation, among primitive people, is almost always a function of the women. In some of these African peoples, the herders form a distinct, superior caste, dominating the agricultural serfs who are descended from war captives.

It has often been suggested that animals may have been domesticated not for utility, but for some religious purpose. Certainly animal sacrifice is widespread among contemporary primitive people, and seems to go back in time as far as any idea can be traced; and certainly, too, this idea would be compatible with the often observed fact that primitive people make surprisingly little use of the domestic animals that they may possess—like the Africans and their cattle mentioned above.

In tropical Asia, where chickens presumably originated, they are said even today to be used by pagan peoples chiefly for sacrifice and for divination, and hardly used for either meat or eggs.

In Islamic and Christian areas of the tropical east, the chief use seems to be for cockfights. Chickens may have achieved their early domestication and wide spread because of their convenience for religious purposes—they were easily available, portable, cheap; and the thighbones, bile sacs, and various other innards were readily adapted to the procedures of divination.

Horses seem to have been used for purposes of prestige, religion and war long before they were put to work with plough or wagon, and even now among the Arab groups who prize them most highly, horses seem to be more of a handicap than a help, and the really useful animals are camels. The extreme of prestige value among animals, and of inconvenience in maintenance, is probably reached by the royal elephants of the East, especially those well-known, god-like white elephants of Siam and Burma.

But white elephants are phenomena of civilization, not of the preliterate cultures that are our present concern. Before getting involved with civilization, I would like to make one more excursion into the origin of things among primitive peoples—looking, this time, into the possible history of metals.

When cultures are classified as food-gathering, hunting, pastoral and agricultural, the varieties are based on the economy of cultures, on the methods whereby the peoples gain their livelihood, their food. This, rightly or wrongly, is used to measure the relative progress of cultures, the relative distance that they have traveled along the path of increasing complexity toward the undefined, unnamed goal of mankind.

Another index of this progress in the preliterate cultural stages is based on the material of tool construction—described by terms like "Stone Age," "Bronze Age," and "Iron Age." We think of the food-gathering people as living in the "Stone Age." Then came a constantly increasing refinement in the chipping and polishing of stone until somewhere, some time, in remote antiquity, the usefulness of metals was discovered, perhaps soon after the first developments of agriculture.

The origins of metal working are as shrouded in mystery as the origins of agriculture. We know the sequence of metal history best for the Mediterranean region, where our own culture arose and where fossil cultures have been subjected to the most intensive study. But the appearance of a given metal in the Mediterranean series helps us very little in determining when or where man discovered how to use that metal. The Iron Age of the Mediterranean, for instance, started around 1000 B.C.; but the metal was mentioned in Chinese records over a thousand years earlier, and appeared as a curiosity in Egypt about 2800 B.C. Yet this is the youngest of the basic metals; for the beginnings of the use of gold, silver, copper and bronze, we can give no dates at all.

We know even less about where than about when these metals were first produced. Copper, gold and silver were used by peoples of both hemispheres; bronze also appeared early in the Andean region of America as well as in China and Egypt of the Old World. All of these metals may first have been worked by tropical peoples, though we associate them, in the Old World at least, with the extra-tropical civilizations of China, the Near East and the Mediterranean.

But iron is the metal of greatest interest to us in the present connection, because there is a considerable amount of evidence that its use may have originated in tropical Africa—a region that we are apt to scorn as a cultural backwash. It is, of course, impossible to prove absolutely that iron smelting was not invented in Asia Minor (where the Hittites would be candidates) or India and carried to Africa in prehistoric times; but it seems at least as likely that it was invented in Africa and exported to the Asiatic cultures way back in the early days of cultures.

Certainly iron smelting is deeply rooted in a great diversity of African peoples, different tribes having different types of smelting techniques, different methods of treating smiths; and iron seems as basic a part of the primitive African ornamentation and economy as gold and copper was in pre-Columbian tropical America.

The whole complicated business of African ore-smelting and iron-working is, of course, disappearing because of the ease with which iron can now be obtained from the Europeans, from the pale-faced creators of industrial civilization, who have learned to handle the forces of steam and electricity. Steam and electricity, clearly, were discovered and harnessed outside of the tropics by peoples of the Western world who thereby, for a time at least, have been able to dominate pretty thoroughly the whole surface of our planet. Since this particular culture has had its immediate origin outside of the tropics, along the shores of the Mediterranean and in the rich forests of central and western Europe, its people have come to regard civilization itself as something essentially and inevitably foreign to the tropics. This thesis is so widely held that its refutation warrants a separate chapter in which we can, with some leisure, examine the incidence within the tropics of this thing called civilization, however defined.

CHAPTER V

★

The Incidence of Civilization

66 C IVILIZATION" is a grand word, one that rolls sonor-
ously off the tongue. It has served orators and writers
well for something like two hundred years now, and
perhaps it should have been left as an ornament of the language
instead of being hauled into the prosaic work-a-day world where
words have to be constricted within their definitions and chained
by their referents. But the historians, anthropologists and sociologists started, some time ago, with the constricting and chaining
process, so that the bright, spell-binding polish of the word has
long been tarnished.

"Civilization" is not an ancient word. It was invented by the
French encyclopaedists of the 18th century as a label for the
emergence of mankind from the barbarism and feudalism of the
Dark Ages. Civilization, to these rationalists, meant enlighten-
ment. They built the word on the Latin adjective *civilis* and noun
civilitas, which came in turn from *civis,* citizen. *Civilitas* implied
politeness and amiability, like our "civility," which would obviously be qualities of the citizen and not of the foreigner, the
barbarian.

The word got into English via James Boswell who reported in
his *Life of Johnson* that "On Monday, March 23, I found him
[Johnson] busy, preparing a fourth edition of his folio dictionary.

. . . He would not admit *civilization,* but only *civility.* With great deference to him, I thought *civilization,* from *to civilize,* better in the sense opposed to *barbarity* than *civility.*"

Clearly all we owe to the encyclopaedists and Boswell is the word, not the meaning, because the anthropological concept of civilization as a culture stage would be quite foreign to eighteenth century thought. Such a meaning, in fact, depends on the application of the ideas of evolution to human affairs, which seems commonplace now, recent though it is in human history. The modern ideas of culture and of cultural evolution might be dated rather neatly from the year 1871, which saw the publication of Darwin's *Descent of Man* and of E. B. Tylor's *Primitive Culture.*

I started to struggle with the problem of definition of civilization in the last chapter, deciding that the primary criterion was writing, which could serve to separate the civilized from the uncivilized, preliterate, primitive cultures. This worked well enough as a crude, first approximation to a definition, but I doubt whether it would stand any very detailed analysis. Even if writing were taken as an absolute token that would serve to distinguish the civilized from the uncivilized, we would still find ourselves with the problem of defining "writing"—where to draw the line between pictures of things and symbols for things or sounds and whether to classify aberrant record systems like the quipus (knotted strings) of the Incas as writing or not. This last serves to illustrate the difficulty of the definition process, since I think everyone would agree that the Incas represent a "civilization," though I would expect no agreement on whether quipus do or do not represent "writing."

Arnold Toynbee, in his *Study of History,* has produced one of the most comprehensive modern studies of civilization, and his use of the word would correspond closely with my usage. It is interesting, then, to find that Toynbee manages to avoid precise definition, using instead a method of case examination. He starts out by attempting to find the limits of the particular civilization to which modern England belongs by searching for the limits of the field that must be covered in order to render English history intelligible. He arrives by this process at the concept of "Western European civilization." He finds four other living civilizations on the planet (Orthodox, Islamic, Hindu and Far Eastern) comparable in being each a separately intelligible field of historical study. By overhauling all of human history in a comparable manner, he comes up with a total of 19 different civilizations (which he later increases to 21). He then is able to learn a great deal about the characteristics of the general species by examining these 19 specimens, without resort to any formal process of definition.

Toynbee contrasts his 19 civilizations with the innumerable specimens known of the other species of human society, the "primitive." As he points out (Vol. I, p. 148), "this preponderance of the primitive societies in numbers is obscured by the equally overwhelming preponderance of the civilizations in their individual dimensions. The two species stand to each other like elephants and rabbits. The primitive societies, in their legions, are relatively short-lived, are restricted to relatively narrow geographical areas, and embrace a relatively small number of human beings either at any given moment or from first to last throughout their histories. The civilizations, whose muster-roll only just rises to double figures, are relatively long-lived, they spread from their original homes over relatively large areas, and the number of human beings that they embrace is relatively great. They spread by exterminating, subjecting or assimilating other societies—sometimes societies of their own species, but primitive societies much more frequently. Primitive societies, like rabbits, have their lives cut short by violence more often than not, and an encounter with some civilization is the way in which violent death commonly overtakes them. As for numbers of human beings . . . it is probable that if we could take a census of the membership of the five living civilizations up to date, during the small number of centuries through which these have yet lived since they first emerged, we should find that each of our Leviathans, singly, has embraced a greater number of human beings already than could be mustered, in the aggregate, by all the primitive societies that have ever existed since the emergence of the Human Race."

I might note that even Toynbee doesn't manage any absolute distinction between his 19 neatly separated specimens of civilized societies and the vast mass of primitive societies, since he is left with a handful of "abortive" and "arrested" civilizations—things like the Vikings, the Polynesians, the Eskimos. A more critical examination of borderline cases and a greater stressing of the anthropological, rather than the historical, point of view, would undoubtedly have greatly increased the number of intermediate or doubtful societies. But however this may be, there is no question but what Toynbee's 19 civilizations correspond closely with the generally accepted extension of the concept of "civilized." Our interest here is to see which of these have occurred in the tropics, and how this tropical occurrence has influenced the general course of man's cultural development.

We could approach this problem of describing the incidence of civilization in the tropics in two different ways—through time and through space. By the first method, we would look to see which civilizations and which elements of civilization had their origin under tropical circumstances. By the second method, we would survey the characteristics of the contemporary civilizations found between the lines of Capricorn and Cancer and see how these compared with the qualities of civilizations to the north (or to the south) of the lines. Either approach would be a very large order, a considerable task of scholarship. So we'll try the impossible—sketching both approaches within the limited space of a single chapter.

I have made a list of Toynbee's 19 specimens of civilization in the accompanying table, in order to give an idea of the variety and of their extension through time and space. Probably no two authorities would agree about the details of such a table. Toynbee himself later in his text adds two more specimens (the Japanese variety of Far Eastern and the Russian variety of Orthodox) to make a grand total of 21; and at the same time he suggests a process whereby the list might be consolidated to make only 11 basically divergent types (Egyptiac, Sumeric, Minoan, Hittite, Sinic, Indic, Syriac, Hellenic, Mayan, Andean and Western).

TOYNBEE'S SPECIMENS OF CIVILIZATION

Name	*Origin:* Time	Place	Parent	Status
Egyptiac	before 4000 B.C.	Nile Valley	none	extinct
Sumeric	before 3500 B.C.	Tigris-Euphrates	none	extinct
Minoan	before 3000 B.C.	Aegean Islands	none	extinct
Babylonic	before 1500 B.C.	Iraq	Sumeric	extinct
Hittite	before 1500 B.C.	Cappadocia	Sumeric	extinct
Sinic	about 1500 B.C.	Yellow River	none	extinct
Indic	about 1500 B.C.	Indus & Ganges	none	extinct
Syriac	before 1100 B.C.	Syria	Minoan	extinct
Hellenic	before 1100 B.C.	Aegean	Minoan	extinct
Mayan	before 500 B.C.	Guatemala	none	extinct
Andean	before Christ	Peru	none	extinct
Far Eastern	before 500 A.D.	China	Sinic	living
Yucatec	about 600 A.D.	Yucatan	Mayan	extinct
Mexic	about 600 A.D.	Mexican highlands	Mayan	extinct
Orthodox	before 700 A.D.	Anatolia	Hellenic	living
Western	before 700 A.D.	Western Europe	Hellenic	living
Hindu	before 800 A.D.	North India	Indic	living
Iranic	before 1300 A.D.	Iran	Syriac ⎫	fused to form
Arabic	before 1300 A.D.	Arabia	Syriac ⎭	living Islamic

At first glance, this list seems to have little to do with the tropics. The place of origin of all fifteen Old World civilizations was, according to Toynbee, outside of the tropics. Tropical origins are, to be sure, ascribed to all four of the New World civilizations, but these seem pretty feeble alongside the glorious profusion of the Mediterranean and Asia. If we examine these Old World civilizations carefully, however, we find that their origins, if outside the tropics, are at least not far outside.

Actually, it seems to me that Toynbee has been far too liberal in allowing for the "independent" development of civilization in different places. Seven of his specimens, five Old World and two New, are given no parentage, and are thus presumed to represent separate passage by different peoples from the primitive to the civilized state of culture. This, I think, is an extreme of "splitting." The extreme of "lumping" would be the position that all civilization is related, that the various traits that go to make the civilized state were each discovered only once, passing by "diffusion" from one part of the world to another. An intermediate position would allow two independent inventions of the whole complex of civilized traits—once for the Old World and once for the New.

Toynbee's dates, too, make a pretty arbitrary sequence, especially the relative antiquity of the Egyptiac, Sumeric, Minoan and Indic. Toynbee himself has pointed out that our wealth of information about the Egyptiac is no reflection of the importance of that culture, but rather of the fact that the climate is particularly favorable for the accumulation of relics, and that this accumulation in turn exerts a compelling attraction on scholars. That Egypt has the oldest dates may, then, merely be another reflection of the fact that Egypt has been the most studied.

There is, actually, no clear evidence as to which of these four cultures is the oldest. At around 3000 B.C., they were all flourishing, and had all reached the level of city-formation—a prime criterion of civilization. Their geographical relation to one another and to the Tropic is shown in the accompanying map, based on a map given by Ralph Turner in his book, *The Great Cultural Traditions*. All four regions were also pretty surely in contact with one another, since articles characteristic of each region have been found in the other regions also, indicating an extensive trade. The Cretans (Minoans), based their civilization on seafaring, and the Indus Valley people seem also to have had ocean-going boats, as well as boats for river traffic.

Two of these culture areas, the Egyptiac and the Indus Valley, touch the Tropic, and surely received important elements from across the line to the south. This is shown by the Abyssinian element among the cultivated plants, and by the importance,

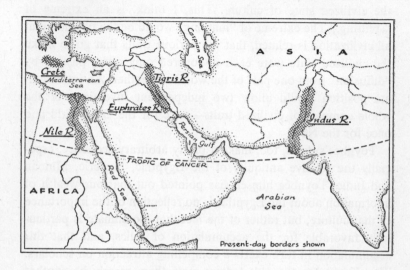

Regions of Old World Civilization, about 3000 B.C.

from the beginning, of tropical products in trade. For the purpose of the thesis of this book I should, of course, like to make out that the cultural level called civilization was first reached somewhere within the tropics, whence it spread at an early period to the river valleys of the Nile, Tigris-Euphrates and Indus. But there isn't any evidence; and the first civilization, the first aggregation of people into cities with storage of food and complex division of labor, the first accumulation and transmission of records and observations through writing, is very generally considered to have occurred in one of these river valleys, spreading fairly early over Asia Minor and the Mediterranean lands, over tropical Asia, and north to the Yellow River and other centers in China. Note, however, that civilization failed to spread very far north, to lands of winter snow and ice, until almost modern times. Indeed, only three of Toynbee's nineteen specimens of the civilized species have ever spread very far north of the Tropic. Those three, however, happen to be the ones that in our day dominate the planet—the Western (led by the democracies of Europe and America), the Orthodox (Russia) and the Far Eastern (China and Japan).

For America there is no argument about the tropical origin of civilization. Indeed, the local civilizations failed ever to spread far outside of the tropics, and no high level of culture was achieved in the north until European man turned up bringing Western European culture with him. I might note in passing that even this Western European culture, for a long time, did better in the tropics than outside on the American continents. The Spaniards were little interested in anything north of Mexico and the West Indies, and when the English and others took to colonizing the higher latitudes (from lack of alternative) their "success" from the point of view of the development of "high" or complex culture was not immediate. Some people, of course, still doubt the applicability of the term "civilized" to the North Americans and the distribution of civilization through the New World would certainly look different to, say, a citizen of Bogotá and a citizen of Cincinnati. But our concern now is with pre-Columbian civilization, with the Mayas and the Incas.

For our knowledge of the Mayas—and for our ignorance—we owe much to Diego de Landa, Bishop of Yucatan. Landa carried out an amazingly thorough job of collecting and burning all of the books or codices of the Maya "as they contained nothing in which there was not to be seen superstition and lies of the devil," so that only three are known to have survived. But he also wrote in considerable detail about the Mayas in his book, *Relación de las Cosas de Yucatan*, giving clues that have helped modern archeologists to decipher the calendar dates of the Mayan monuments.

Regions of pre-Columbian Civilization in the New World.

The three codices known to have survived Landa's zeal were all found in Europe, chance souvenirs brought home by some conquistador or other. Unfortunately, these three chance survivors are of very little use in helping to understand the Mayas. One, apparently, is a treatise on astronomy; another is a manual on ritual and ceremony; and the third a compilation of horoscopes to aid priests in making divination. The earliest Spanish writers are all in agreement that the Mayas kept records of their history in these books of hieroglyphs. If only something of these histories had survived, together with a key to the deciphering!

These Mayan books are, themselves, of considerable archeological interest. They were made from the bark of a kind of wild fig tree, which was pounded into a pulp and held together with some natural gum as a bonding substance; a long strip of this was coated on both sides with a wash of fine, white lime. The strip was then folded like a screen, and glyphs and pictures were painted on both sides. This method of book manufacture is closely similar to a method used in Indonesia (Sumatra) and forms one of the similarities—perhaps too numerous to be catalogued as coincidences—between New World and Old World cultures.

The bookmaking may resemble that of Sumatra, but the kind of writing within the Mayan books seems to be unique. The Mayan glyphs are "ideographic," each character being a conventionalized symbol for some idea. I like Morley's illustration of this, that in Chinese writing "the ideograph for 'trouble' is the conventionalized symbol for a woman, repeated twice, standing under a gate, and the ideograph for 'war,' the symbols for three women standing under the same gate." Apparently the Mayan glyphs had no phonetic significance, being thus more primitive than even the oldest known Egyptian hieroglyphs.

The only well understood part of Mayan writing, however, is the numeral system and the calendar; truly remarkable inventions. The clue to reading these was given by Bishop Landa, and the unraveling carried out by a series of brilliant and industrious modern archeologists. The zero date, the beginning of time, for this Mayan calendar, would be 3113 B.C. Archeologists consider this to be a purely hypothetical date, and for various reasons consider that the Mayan system was actually invented about 300 B.C. The earliest known objects believed to be marked with contemporary dates are, however, much later even than this: a jade plaque bearing a date corresponding to 320 A.D., and a monument (Stela 9 at Uaxactun) dated 328 A.D. Dated monuments, after this, become frequent, and archeologists divide Mayan history into an Old Empire period, lasting until about A.D. 1000, with the major cities in Guatemala; and a New Empire period, with the major cities in Yucatan. This New Empire disintegrated in an internecine war which culminated in 1441 with the sack of the city of Mayapan and the collapse of centralized authority. Historians thus generally consider that Mayan civilization was already finished at the time of the Spanish conquest (1527–1546).

The Aztec empire that Cortes found in the highlands of Mexico was, of course, an offshoot of this Mayan civilization— but a militarized, degenerate offshoot, characterized by blood-soaked warriors and blood-soaked priests.

Way to the south, in the mountains of Peru, Pizarro found and looted the other great American civilization, the Empire of the Incas, children of the sun. This was a very different affair from the Maya-Aztec development, and archeologists generally consider the two to have had quite independent origins. The Incas had no writing, only the complicated quipu system of knotted strings for keeping records and accounts, and they consequently have left no series of dated monuments to aid in the reconstruction of their history. This complete divergence in method of record keeping, which we have taken to be the essential base for the distinction of the civilized from the uncivilized, would seem in itself to prove the independence of the two cultural developments.

All students agree in classing the Inca as a civilization, in full flower at the time of the conquest. They built great cities, held together by a system of authority and administration comparable with the similar products of Roman genius; and their emphasis, as with the Romans, was on communication, on the development

Examples of Mayan Glyphs. The signs for the months as used
on the monuments: the Mayan calendar year consisted of 18
months of 20 days each, and one closing month of 5 days.
(After Gann and Thompson.)

of magnificent roads and courier services. The inhabitants of their wide realm, which covered much of modern Peru, Bolivia, Ecuador and part of Colombia, lived in greater peace and security than any they have enjoyed since their conquest by the Spaniards; and travel was far safer and far faster than it was again until the advent of the airplane. Even this qualification might be left out, since the usefulness of the airplane is limited among these mountain fastnesses.

As Mangelsdorf and Reeves remark, "the government of the Incas was one of the most sensible and successful which has ever been developed. Paternalistic, but practical in its paternalism, it required that every inhabitant do his share and in return it guaranteed him a share in the necessities of life while permitting him wide latitude in the affairs of the family, the community, and the practice of his religion. When disaster befell one region of the Empire, assistance was immediately forthcoming from other regions. The ever normal granary was an accomplished fact in Peru, centuries before it received serious consideration by the 'advanced' American civilization of today."

The Incan culture itself is considered to have had its beginnings rather recently, about 1100 A.D., but it was based upon three prior Andean cultures of considerable complexity, the Chimu and Nasca of the coast and the Tiuahuanaco of the highlands, and these may go back to great antiquity. It would seem, certainly, that a considerable stretch of time must have been needed for the development of the skills in engineering and in agriculture shown by these people.

The engineering feats of the Andean people are remarkable enough; but their skill in agriculture, though its consequences remain less spectacular than the great masonry walls of the fortress cities, was even more extraordinary. Possibly they cultivated more different kinds of edible plants than any other people before modern times. I have made no comparative lists, so this is put forward as a very tentative suggestion; but even a short selection from the Andean catalogue shows the diversity of their crops and the extent of our debt: maize, beans, squashes, cassava (the source of modern tapioca), sweet potatoes, cotton, tobacco, peppers, tomatoes, peanuts, potatoes. They also domes-

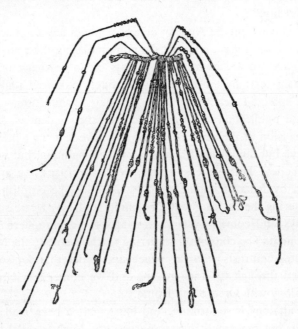

A *Quipu*: the Record Device of the Incas.

ticated several animals—the llama, the alpaca and the guinea pig—which contrasts with the Mayan failure to domesticate animals. To quote Mangelsdorf and Reeves again, "every square foot of tillable soil was utilized and in addition agriculture was pushed far up the steep slopes by the use of masonry terraces. Fish and guano were used as fertilizer, and water was supplied in many places by an elaborate system of irrigation which tapped the streams sometimes far above the agricultural lands, and carried the water by aqueducts to the higher terraces from which it was led by successive steps to the lower fields. The Andean region is the only place in America where agriculture generally had passed beyond the exploitative stage and where the soils were systematically built up rather than carelessly depleted of their fertility."

The Mayan and the Andean civilizations, in any such account as this, stand in great contrast. In contemplating the remains of the Mayas, we are impressed by feats of an aesthetic or contemplative sort: by the exquisite and finely balanced sculpture, by the splendid beauty of much of their architecture, by the immense intellectual accomplishment of their calendar, by the fine precision of their mathematics. We have lost their literature and have but tantalizing fragments of their painting, but we can easily believe both were splendid. With the Incas, we are impressed by feats of engineering, by practical accomplishments in mastering the environment for definite ends: by fortresses and highways and courier systems and all of the paraphernalia of government. The constantly recurring warfare among the Mayan city-states contrasts with the peace and order that for so long prevailed through the Inca realm; and we come, inevitably, to the analogy with Greece and Rome.

The analogy is so striking, and has so often been made, that I cannot but presume it has some validity. Such parallel trends may have some root in the accidents of physical environment or of cultural history; and speculation about relationships is certainly not to be dismissed as fruitless. But our information, for America, is discouragingly fragmentary when compared with the abundance of our knowledge of the Mediterranean—inadequate though even this may be. Light on the meaning of history, on the causation of man's varied and tortuous progress, is thus more likely to come from studies of Hellenic civilization than from analyses of developments in the American tropics. But the Hellenists can at least remember that the shores of the Mediterranean do not constitute all of the world—that there is, besides Athens and Rome, Copan and Cuzco to be accounted for.

This account of tropical American civilization should be balanced by some account of the development of civilization in the Old World tropics: but this is rendered difficult by the complexity of the materials and by my own lack of firsthand acquaintance with the region. Furthermore, in Asia the distinction between tropical and non-tropical loses much of its meaning because the line of the Tropic of Cancer cuts quite arbitrarily through the Asiatic land mass, and equally arbitrarily through the development of Asiatic history. Essentially, however, ancient tropical civilization in this region involves peninsular India, Ceylon, Burma, Siam, Cambodia, the Malay States, Sumatra and Java.

As I pointed out earlier, the valleys of the Indus and Ganges rivers form one of the earliest known regions of Old World civilization. These lie just to the north of the Tropic, and they are not separated from the rich lands to the south by any barrier of mountain, desert or sea, so that one can presume that culture of a civilized level spread very soon into truly tropical territory —if, indeed, it did not originate in the tropics and spread north into these valleys. The traces of such early cultures have, however, been obscured by the continuous occupation of the country by a dense and industrious population who have continuously utilized the materials left by their ancestors, and by the tropical climate, which does not favor the survival of human constructions. It is striking that the remains of earliest civilization are very frequently found in arid or semiarid regions—like the Indus Valley, the Euphrates Valley or Egypt—and much has been made of this by cultural historians. But in judging this, I think we should always keep in mind that an arid or semiarid climate is particularly favorable to the preservation of the remains of early civilization; while the climate of the tropical forest regions is particularly unfavorable. Perhaps the conditions that we judge favorable to civilization are, in part at least, merely favorable to the preservation of the traces of civilization.

Cultures of a civilized level have unquestionably existed for a very long time in the Asiatic tropics, and their very antiquity and complexity makes analysis difficult. And often all that we have left on which to build reconstruction is the record in stone consisting of sculptured figures rather than inscriptions. The early oriental cultures seem to have been little interested in recording the events of contemporary history: they were preoccupied rather with the gods and the paraphernalia of religion and written historical materials do not become abundant until the advent of Muslim influence around 1000 A.D.

For our purpose of historical perspective on the incidence of civilization in the tropics, two of the most interesting oriental examples are the extinct civilizations of Ceylon and Cambodia, since these, like the Mayan example, show that a very high level of culture can be attained under tropical forest conditions. Though with these, as with the Mayan, the governing forces of both the rise and the fall are obscure.

Ceylon is a large island (just a little smaller than Ireland) lying at the tip of the Indian peninsula, between 6 and 10 degrees north of the equator. Its fame reached even to the classic Greeks, who called it Taprobane, placing it on their maps at the far margin of the oikoumene, the habitable world. More or less definite records of local history start in the fifth century B.C. with the chronicles of the Mahawansa, which give circumstantial details of the reigns of a long line of Sinhalese kings from the founding of the capital city of Anuradhapura. There is a tradition that Buddha himself visited the island, but Buddhism did not become the predominant religion until about 300 B.C. A branch of the sacred Bo-tree was brought from Magadha and planted in Anuradhapura in 288 B.C.—one of the dates on which all authorities seem to agree.

These Sinhalese developed a remarkable civilization, lost now in forest wastes, that depended essentially on the building up of great reservoirs for the storage of water from the seasonal rains. Their civilization apparently lasted as long as they were able to maintain this agricultural system and collapsed with the repeated breaking of the dikes in the course of internecine wars among local princes in the thirteenth and fourteenth centuries. Indian princes invaded and annexed the island on several occasions, and in 1408 it was invaded by a Chinese army, remaining tributary to China for 30 years. The last of the great local princes was Prakrama Bahu, who gained control of the whole island in 1155. This king was a fanatic builder of palaces, monasteries, temples and suchlike useless structures, and one theory of the collapse of the island's civilization blames the enormous strain that these activities must have placed upon the economy, which thereafter followed a steady down-grade course.

The temples, palaces, and dagobas of Ceylon seem impressive enough, but they pale beside the magnificence that the archeologists have found in the forests of Cambodia, the remains of the civilization of the Khmers. Almost all we know of these people is the record they left in stone—the great temple of Angkor Vat, the sprawling ruins of the vast, nearby city of Angkor Thom, and nearly a hundred other sites of cities and temples scattered through the forests of the Mekong Valley and on the margins of the great lake, Tonle Sap. The Khmers clearly represent an offshoot of Hindu civilization, with no sign of Chinese influence, though the region would seem as accessible from China as from India. One tradition has the Khmer Empire founded by Prea-Thang, son of a sovereign of Indrapat (the modern Delhi), who was banished from home in the fifth century A.D.

However founded, the Khmer Empire must have been prosperous and vigorous to support these grand cities and temples; and intellectually adventurous to develop what many authorities consider one of the finest flowerings of Hindu art. This culture endured for some five hundred years, collapsing in the tenth century from causes that are, as far as I can gather, completely unknown. The civilization of modern Cambodia seems to stem from quite different sources and to have developed along quite different lines, not even occupying the territory of the Khmers, which has been left again to the forest.

If, then, we surveyed the world a thousand years ago, we would find much of man's greatest achievement within the tropics. The great empires of the Mayas, the Incas, the Khmers and the Sinhalese would seem to hold the key to the future, rather than the warring fragments of Christendom, falling back around the Mediterranean before the mighty surge of Islam. But Europe, in the passing thousand years, discovered new sources of power, developed a new variant of civilization based on iron (which may have been learned from the Africans), on gunpowder (from the Chinese), on printing (fumbled with by many people). The keys to knowledge somehow escaped from the priesthood into the hands of the merchants, the bankers and the industrialists. And this Western civilization, accumulating this new power, burst outward in the sixteenth and seventeenth centuries to brand in some degree, all of the multitude of other cultures that had been developing indigenously behind their barriers of seas and mountains and deserts.

Today, if we survey the world, we find the mark of Western civilization everywhere. Whether this is "good" or "bad" is beside the point. For our present purposes, however, it is important to note that Western civilization had its origins outside the tropics, and that it has nowhere been notably successful in establishing itself in any pure form within the tropics. Latin America represents the only large-scale direct transplant, since the local cultures withered away almost completely with the Western touch.

Most Europeans would regard Latin America as "backward." But they regarded the United States as backward fifty years ago, and they are still rather reluctant to admit American accomplishment in what they would regard as the finer aspects of civilization. Latin America certainly has not contributed greatly to the main stream of Western development, but this surely stems from complex causes. Latin America might possibly be used to support the thesis that Western civilization, in its pure form, is not readily adaptable to tropical conditions; but this is hardly damning except to those who consider the Western variety to be the only possible form of civilization in general. Latin American culture is, in fact, most interesting in the ways and places where it has diverged from the typical Western, picking up elements from the local environment, as in the development of Mexican art.

Western culture has brought little to tropical Africa except disease, administrators and missionaries. Africa, then, left out in the survey of past civilizations, can also be omitted from our sketch of the present.

So we come to the present situation of civilization in tropical Asia, with the bold plan of covering the ground in a paragraph or two. Asia now clearly is resurgent, and it is no longer a question of whether Western culture will in the end prevail there; the question rather is what traces of the West will be left there, and whether in the long run the West will be overwhelmed by some Asiatic variety of the species civilization.

India and Indonesia have shaken off the political dominance of the West, but they have copied the Western idea of national states and of an industrial economy. How this will blend with their own traditions remains to be seen. Perhaps the brew will prove a fatal poison; perhaps the forest will grow again in Bombay and Batavia as it has in Angkor Thom and Anuradhapura. But in that case surely the cities of Europe and America will also give way to the waiting seeds of oak, because all of the diverse civilizations of the planet must surely now stand or fall together.

On the other hand it may be that these pleasant peoples of the tropics will be able to take the best things that the West has found and blend them with the fine accomplishments of their own past cultures to find, south of Cancer, a new way of life that will avoid the extremes of despotism and misery as their climate avoids the extremes of heat and cold.

The way in which civilization develops in the tropics will depend, I think, on many factors of cultural adaptation to the environmental conditions, including climate. I want to discuss this problem of the relationship between climate and civilization at some length. But before going into this, I think it would be advisable to devote some space to the description of the actual climatic conditions that are found within the tropical zone.

CHAPTER VI

★

On Tropical Climates

THE Tropical Zone is bounded on the north by the Tropic of Cancer and on the south by the Tropic of Capricorn— a fixed astronomical and geographical matter that is subject to change only through astronomical changes such as the precession of the equinoxes. This seems a clear and sensible definition. But by lines of reasoning that are probably equally sensible, a quite different definition can be arrived at. By the astronomical definition, Havana is in the tropics and Key West not. Yet the climate of the two places differs hardly at all, though we presume the tropics to represent a climatic zone. People living on the lower east coast of Florida often claim that their region is tropical, and scientists studying human physiology under tropical conditions have been known to pick Florida as the place to carry out their studies.

The concept that would get southeast Florida inside of the tropics is based on temperature lines. Thus according to Ellsworth Huntington, the region of tropical climate should be defined in terms of the mean annual temperature, and he would place the boundary at the annual isotherm of 70° F. (21° C.). Another group of geographers would define the tropics not in terms of the annual mean, but in terms of the mean temperature of the coolest month. One system of this sort would place within

85

the tropics all regions in which the coolest month has an average temperature of over 18° C. (64.4° F.).

Actually, these various mean temperature lines, or isotherms, stick fairly close to the astronomical lines of Cancer and Capricorn. Some geographers claim that the astronomical lines are arbitrary, but they are very real in terms of hours of light per day and angle of sunlight, as important in climate as is temperature. The isotherms, it seems to me, are also arbitrary. "Mean temperatures" are abstractions, as every gardener knows. The mean temperature for May over a period of ten years is no help if deviation from the mean in the shape of a frost occurs this May.

The isotherm, like the tropic, becomes a line on the map, and has to be drawn somewhere. Thus, in the case of Florida, the use of the coolest month would put Fort Pierce inside the tropics, and Vero, fifteen or so miles north, outside. Ellsworth Huntington's system of using the 70° F. annual isotherm would place the line somewhere between Jacksonville and Saint Augustine: though no resident of Miami would admit Saint Augustine to be tropical, and few would concede Forth Pierce, or anything else north of Dade County. The astronomical system at least has the merit of avoiding tourist-oriented squabbles.

We can concede a "tropical-like" climate to southeastern Florida, if that is what they want. But I should think "subtropical" would be a better adjective, since it could be made selective, allowing the desired things like "tropical flowers" and excluding the undesired like "tropical diseases."

If we were trying to review here the general subject of the climates of the earth, we would have to become involved with isotherms, since outside of the tropics, temperature lines become tremendously important. But we are limiting discussion to the tropics, and once the line of Cancer has been crossed, isotherms have very little meaning. The climate types within the tropics depend primarily on rainfall, and temperature rears its ugly head only in matters of detail like studies of zonation on mountains.

Men within the tropics may fuss about the temperature—but usually it's the relative humidity that is bothering them, or else they have too many clothes on.

The relative unimportance of temperature changes within the

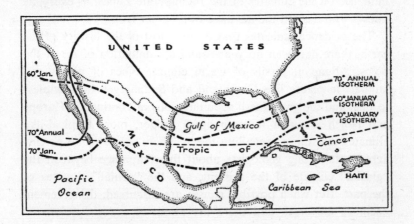

tropics and their tremendous importance over the rest of the earth gains in interest if viewed with the perspective of geological history. The general climate of the earth today is "glacial," but this type of climate has only prevailed for very short times during the history of the earth—for perhaps one per cent of the period for which there is a fossil record. During most of its history, the climate of the earth as a whole has been what the geologists call the "genial" type, the sort of climate that we may now enjoy only within the equatorial region.

We all know something nowadays about the history of the Pleistocene ice sheets that covered most of Europe and North America at various times during the most recent period of geological history. Geologists calculate that the last of these continental ice sheets started to retreat about 30,000 years ago, a mere moment in geological time, and they date "recent" or contemporary history from the beginning of this ice retreat. The remnants of the last glaciation are still with us in the form of the polar icecaps, the great glacier of Greenland, and various isolated glaciers in many parts of the world. These remnants, especially the polar icecaps, are still large enough to exert a controlling influence on the climates of the Intemperate Zones, as everyone knows who has felt the advance of a "polar front."

The evidence indicates that during most of the history of the earth, there has been no year-round accumulation of ice at the poles. Abundant fossils of warm climate types of plants and animals in places like Greenland and Spitzbergen bear witness to this; and the great fossil accumulations of continental Europe and North America indicate much milder, more tropical-like climates that those prevailing today. There seems to be no disagreement among geologists about this difference between the "glacial" climate of the present, and the "genial" climates of the past. But when possible causes are discussed, disagreement becomes universal, and there are about as many opinions as there are geologists.

A review of these theories would be out of place here. The interested reader can find all of the details in the book by C. E. P. Brooks, *Climate Through the Ages.* I do want to emphasize, though, the agreement among students that some very slight change—in solar radiation, in the earth's air temperature, in the gaseous composition of the atmosphere—might lead to very far-reaching effects as ice started to carry over from one year to the next at the poles. For, as has often been pointed out, ice represents a storage of coldness that can become cumulative. As Brooks remarks, "the real difference between the center of Africa and the center of Antarctica is that in the former, water is water and in the latter, water is ice."

"Glacial" climates have been associated, all through geological history, with periods of uplift, and lofty mountains in themselves cause diversification of climate. We are living now in a period of mountain building that is probably as active as any that the earth has known since life became established. Conditions on the planet in times past, then, were surely much more uniform than now. But these geological changes have been greatest in the higher latitudes, and the equatorial belt has probably had a relatively stable history with a climatic continuity unknown elsewhere. This is important, I think, in interpreting biological conditions in the tropics.

Before abandoning this excursion into geological background, I would like to include a few remarks on climatic history during "recent" times, since this bears on the various theories of "climate and civilization." As mentioned above, geologists date "recent" from the beginning of the last glacial retreat, which they presume to have started about 30,000 years ago. The civilization of man, then, has occurred in the course of this retreat, and might well be related to consequent climatic changes.

The evidence of climatic change during the first part of the period of glacial retreat (from 30,000 or 40,000 to 12,000 B.C.) is purely geological, and indicates a fairly regular glacial recession from an extreme with tundra vegetation as far south as northern Spain in Europe, and New Jersey, Missouri and Iowa in North America. From 12,000 B.C. to 120 B.C., there is a fairly clear record of minor climatic oscillations in western and central Europe, with both archeological and paleontological evidence. From 120 B.C. to the middle of the nineteenth century there is documentary evidence of climatic swings, and since the middle of the nineteenth century there are instrumental records—for too short a period to be of real help.

The evidence for climatic change has been studied most carefully in Europe. It depends on things like the painstaking analysis of silt deposits in Scandinavia, on the changes in size and salinity of the Baltic Sea, on archeological studies of the lake dweller remains in Switzerland, on the clues left by the retreating glaciers. Civilization, in the meanwhile, was taking form in northern India, Asia Minor and the Nile Valley, and the relation of the

European climatic sequence to the Asiatic cultural sequence thus involves a lot of supposition.

In general, climatic changes from 12,000 B.C. to the present seem not to have been drastic. Their clearest effect on man's activities was in high latitudes: the colonization of Greenland from 984 to 1410, for instance, was pretty surely related to warm conditions involving glacial retreat during that period. The correlation of these high latitude changes with events in human history and prehistory in other parts of the world—with the development of Mayan civilization in the tropics or anything of that sort—seems very tenuous indeed. About the most that we can say is that since there is clear evidence of various sorts of climatic change in the European area, we cannot take for granted climatic constancy in other parts of the world. But Pleistocene temperature changes in the tropics appear very unlikely indeed, though there may well have been considerable shifts in rainfall, especially in the trade wind latitudes which are now predominantly arid—and where the human cultural stage called civilization may first have been reached.

Our interest in this book, however, is not so much with the presumed climates of the past as with the actual climates of the present—a complicated enough subject. Fortunately, conditions are less complex in the tropics than in higher latitudes. Polar fronts, for instance, do not need to worry us. They do sometimes push intemperate weather southward, so that you wish you had a fireplace in Cuba or a sweater in Honduras. But the easy way out is to treat that not as climate, but as weather. Weather in the tropics, as in California and Florida, is always exceptional, a transient embarrassment that most frequently coincides with visitors.

Climate, of course, goes on all of the time, while weather changes from day to day. Climate, in other words, is the average of the weather—for a particular place, for a region or zone, or for the earth's surface in general. There is, it seems to me, a regional difference in emphasis here. We spend a lot of time talking about both weather and climate, but in New England the weather is more often discussed, while in California and Florida people are preoccupied with the climate. In New England the day-to-day changes are uppermost in people's minds, while in lower latitudes the general trends, the average conditions of a particular place, are of most concern. The distinction is strengthened when the line of Cancer has been crossed, so that there is some justification for treating weather as a phenomenon of the Intemperate Zone, climate as a property of the Tropics.

Particular tropical climates are the result of two sorts of factors, one that might be called "astronomical," and the other "topographical." The astronomical factors would have the field all to themselves if the earth's surface were uniform; as it is, they set the basic pattern which the mountains and seas and land masses modify locally to a varying extent. This hypothetical uniform earth would have an atmospheric circulation like that sketched in the diagram on the following page.

The angle of the earth causes the rays of the sun to fall more directly on the equatorial than on the polar regions. As a result, the air at the equator is warmed more rapidly than elsewhere and, according to the well-known behavior of warm air, rises; this expanding warm air flows poleward aloft, resulting in an increased weight of air over the poles. Hence the equatorial low pressure areas and the polar highs. The earth, of course, is constantly rotating on its axis from west to east and this sets up deflections and eddies in the returning air near the surface. The general result is a secondary low pressure area at about 60° (the subpolar low), and a secondary high pressure at about 30° (the horse latitudes), with prevailing east winds in the polar regions and near the equator (the polar easterlies and the trades), and prevailing west winds in the middle latitudes (the westerlies).

The "equator" of the above account is, of course, the "heat equator," which wanders back and forth between Capricorn and

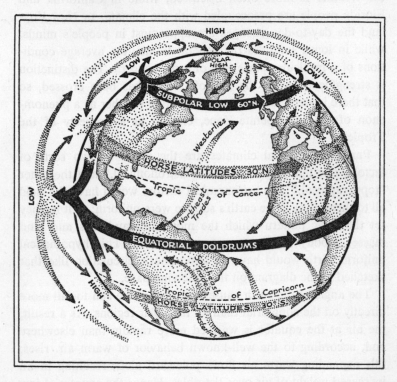

Schematic Diagram of Atmospheric Circulation (after Osborn).

Cancer with the annual journey of the sun, with resulting seasonal shifts in the pattern of the doldrums and the trades.

The warm air, rising in the equatorial regions, loses its capacity to hold water as it cools with altitude, which makes the region of the equatorial doldrums one of high rainfall. The descending air of the horse latitudes, on the other hand, is dry; and since this is the air of the trade winds, the trade wind regions tend to be dry, either permanently (as deserts) or seasonally while the trade winds are blowing.

This basic "astronomical" pattern is greatly modified by the topographical features of the earth's surface, and both classes of factors have to be taken into account in explaining the climate of any given place or region. The most important element in the description of any tropical climate is rainfall, so this will be given most of our attention. Amount of rain is basic not only for the comparison of the climate of one place with that of another within the tropics, but also for the description of the annual parade of seasons at any given place. Total annual rainfall varies from about 400 inches to zero, and this rainfall may be fairly evenly distributed through the year, or there may be a dry season and a wet season, or there may be a double alternation of two wet and two dry seasons.

The total amount of rain and its seasonal distribution controls the type of vegetation, so climate and vegetation types go together. For most purposes it is convenient to differentiate between four basic types of climate (and vegetation), though each of these main types can be split into many subdivisions, useful for special study purposes. The basic types are: humid (forest), subhumid (grassland), semiarid (steppe), and arid (desert).

The tropical humid climate is, essentially, the rain forest climate. Since rain forest—jungle—is almost synonymous with tropics in most people's minds, it will get a chapter by itself. The definition of rain forest climate varies with different authors, but it involves a rainfall of at least 150 inches a year, fairly evenly distributed through the twelve months. A lower annual rainfall than this in the tropics is almost always associated with a definite dry season, resulting in less luxuriant forests, or in a mixture of forest and savannah, and representing the subhumid, or grassland type.

From the accompanying map of tropical climates, it can be seen that the rain forest (humid) climate follows the equatorial

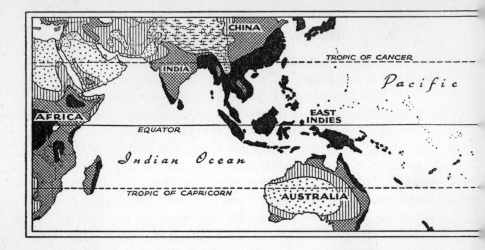

doldrums around the world, occurring in the Amazon drainage of South America, the Congo drainage of Africa, and in Malaya and the East Indies of the Asiatic tropics. Local conditions result in rain forest climates farther away from the equator in a few places, like the Caribbean coast of Central America.

The subhumid and semiarid tropical climates flank the equatorial rain forest around the globe. The subhumid climate is often called the "monsoon climate" and it characterizes latitudes where the trade winds blow monotonously for months at a time. The earth will be parched for a few months by these dry winds, and then drenched with torrential rains that turn the dust of roads to bottomless mud. The vegetation often is grass on the hills and forest in the lowlands and along the streams. Or large areas may be covered by deciduous forest, by trees of many species that drop their leaves during the hot dry season.

In the semiarid climate forests disappear, and isolated trees become scarcer. The weather is dry for most of the year. The semiarid climate grades imperceptibly into the arid, or desert, type where vegetation is either very highly specialized or absent altogether.

There are seven generally recognized tropical deserts, all on the margins of the tropics, on the lines of either Capricorn or

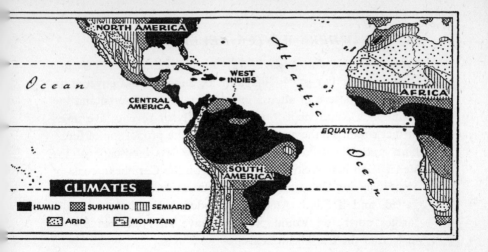

Cancer. The seven are: the Sahara and the Kalihari in Africa, the Thar and the Arabian in Asia, the Victoria in Australia, the Atacama-Peruvian in South America, and the Colorado-Sonoran in Mexico. They cover all of the land surface of the tropical zone where the trade winds blow all year round. This is because the trades always blow toward the equator, from cooler to warmer latitudes; the resultant warming increases the water-carrying capacity of the air, and makes for drying winds. Windward coasts flanked by mountains are exceptions; such coasts, instead of being desert, may have a very heavy rainfall because the trade winds, in rising over the mountains, get cooled.

Which brings us to the matter of tropical mountains, where temperature must be taken into account in defining climate.

I had a chance to get a firsthand acquaintance with tropical mountain climates during the eight years that I lived in the Colombian town of Villavicencio. The town was built at the very base of the great mountain range of the Eastern Andes. The vast interior plain of South America, veined by the gradually converging tributaries of the Orinoco and Amazon drainage systems, lay to the east of us. There we could see, in almost schematic form, the basic system of tropical climates. Our latitude was 4° north of the equator, which put us in the zone where the equatorial rain forest gave way to the subhumid grassland climate. Directly east of Villavicencio, the plain was covered by a complex pattern of alternating savannahs and forests, and the continuous Amazonian forest started fifty or seventy-five miles farther south. To the north, in this plain, the proportion of forest land gradually decreased toward the treeless landscape of the Venezuelan llanos. Still farther north, on the Caribbean coast of Venezuela and Colombia, semiarid, almost desert conditions prevailed, and if South America extended a few hundred miles farther north, we would probably have an American Sahara instead of the Caribbean Sea.

The towering Andes rose directly behind our town, with no nonsense like foothills. During the first twenty minutes of driving on the road to Bogotá, we climbed out of the "tropics" into the "subtropics," out of the rain forest into the cloud forest, where the fluffy cumulus clung as grey fog on the mountainside, where the atmosphere was perpetually damp and cool. This particular road then wound through a river valley where man long ago destroyed the vegetation. If, however, we had been able to continue directly up the mountainside, as I have done elsewhere on foot, we would have entered the "temperate zone" at about eight thousand feet which, at eleven or twelve thousand feet would give way to the fantastic "elfin woodland" of tropical mountains—a cold fairyland of stunted, twisted trees overburdened with moss and lichens, of startlingly beautiful alpine flowers hidden away among the boulders. Higher still comes the páramo zone, cold, bleak and very comparable with the arctic tundra. It is not much farther to perpetual snow, which begins at altitudes between 16,000 and 18,000 feet in the tropics, depending on local conditions.

We could thus, at any time, drive from the year-long August of Villavicencio to the year-long November of Bogotá (at 8600 feet), where the thermometer dropped down toward the freezing point every night, though it rarely actually reached this freezing point. The mountains around Bogotá do not rise as far as the snow line, but in other parts of Colombia we could have left the road and walked on up the mountains into January, though I could never see that January offered enough incentive to warrant the effort.

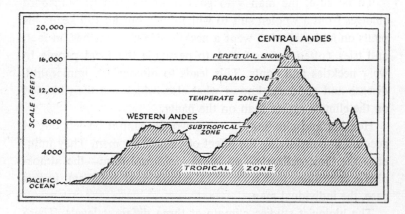

Profile of the Andes in Colombia to Show the Zoning of Mountain Climates (after Chapman).

The term "tropical climate" has little meaning, then, if climates in the tropics range from rain forest to desert, from perpetually hot to perpetually cold. To say that a place is in the tropics tells us little about its climate. We know that its longest day of sunlight will be less than 14 hours, its shortest day more than 10 hours and that it will not have strong seasonal temperature contrasts. That is about all.

Yet we often talk about "the tropical climate," and we no doubt will continue to do so. We mean a hot and sticky climate, which would be an equatorial, lowland, maritime climate—something like Panama or Singapore. This is generally considered to be unpleasant, enervating, unhealthy and all the rest. I plan to discuss the physiological effects of climate in the next chapter, but I cannot resist pointing out here that these words represent judgments of people who have transferred climates, from London to Singapore or New York to Panama, without making any very radical transfer of habits, clothes, housing, diet, or any of the other numerous similar cultural elements.

To be sure, the man who goes from London to Singapore changes from a woolen suit to white duck, but he still keeps his pants on and may even wear a necktie. He goes further, in fact, and tries (often successfully) to persuade the local people to wear neckties and pants. This leads to discomfort, immorality, disease and goodness knows what else, which are then blamed on the climate rather than on the pants.

Housing and clothing, in other words, cannot be left out of account in considering the effect of climate on man. They influence the "microclimate," to use a biological term—the atmospheric conditions that surround the individual organism, in this case, the individual man.

The biologist studies climate at three different levels. There is first the geographical or regional climate, the sort of thing that can be measured in standard meteorological stations and that has been the subject of discussion so far in this chapter. Then, at the second level, there is the climate of the habitat—the climatic environment of the forest, meadow or stream where the organism spends most of its time. And finally, at the third level, we have the climate surrounding the individual organism, the environmental conditions around the blade of grass on which a grasshopper is sitting, or under the rock where a beetle is hiding, or inside the hollow log where an opossum spends the day.

If you like to call things by names derived from the Greek language, you can call these the "geoclimate," the "ecoclimate" and the "microclimate." Of these, "microclimate" is perhaps the most useful, because it emphasizes the fact that atmospheric conditions, as they affect the individual organism, may be quite different from the atmospheric conditions studied by the meteorologists, and that they must be studied by special methods and often with special instruments.

Some of the characteristics of ecological climates, of habitat climates, will be brought out in a later chapter, in describing environmental conditions within the tropical rain forest. These ecological climates are probably of little direct relevance for civilized man, since he quite promptly destroys local vegetation formations by activities like clearing forests and draining swamps; though he does create new habitat climates in the process of building towns and cities, and of laying out patterns of cultivation.

The most drastic effects of human activity, however, are at the level of microclimate—in the effect of the clothes that each man wears, of the way he builds the houses that he lives in. These matters are sufficiently interesting, in relation to tropical adaptations, to warrant a chapter to themselves.

C H A P T E R   V I I

★

Clothes Make the Man

M Y serious thinking about the adaptation of clothes to the tropics started many years ago, on an occasion that I still remember clearly. It was on a hot night in Port-au-Prince at a governmental reception to which, through some fluke of diplomacy, I had been invited. It was a full dress affair—the men wore white tie and tails. I was acutely miserable and, watching the people about me, it seemed that the misery was general where not glossed over by liberal application of alcohol. It was truly ridiculous to see some splendid specimen of the black race all decked out in this English finery, constrained within starch and braces and trousers, vainly trying to stem the streams of sweat—though obviously proud of the civilization thus shown by his city and his country. It was even more ridiculous to see the pallid specimens of my own race mopping their brows, to see the gradual wilting of their shirts and to hear their complaints—not about the clothes, but about the climate.

The Haitians were right, of course. If their government had issued invitations, beautifully engraved upon the snowiest of cards, with the notation "loinclothes will be worn," their nation would have been dismissed from the councils of the civilized world as the horrified ministers of this and that trousered power suspended all communication. The New York banks would have withdrawn their loans, but this would be no blessing because gunboats would have promptly appeared in the harbor to re-enforce the development of some form of government capable of recognizing the amenities of diplomatic courtesy.

This is no special peeve of mine about dress clothes, because some of my pleasantest memories are of affairs in European capitals where I was dressed in the same outfit. True, I have never really been at ease in a starched collar, but otherwise dress clothes seemed comfortable enough in London, once I had learned the trick of wearing a heavy undershirt as an insurance against the times when I had to leave the vicinity of the fireplace. A London reception in a loincloth would be as uncomfortable as the Haitian one in a white tie.

It's a queer business, this matter of the clothing habits of mankind, and obviously not susceptible of explanation on any rational grounds. I believe that anthropologists now generally agree that clothes had their origin not as a protection against weather, nor in relation to any developing sense of modesty or shame, but as part of man's search for adornment, which in turn may have been rooted in primitive magical practises. The explanation of clothes, then, would be tied up with the explanation of body painting, tattooing, tooth-chipping, hair arrangement, skull deformation, and all of the other practices through which man attempts to improve or change his appearance.

Unfortunately we shall never be able to reconstruct the clothing sequence of ancient primitive man as we have been able to reconstruct the cultural sequence of stone tools because clothes differ from stone implements in that they are not readily preserved. But we know that clothing is at least as old as civilization, from the records in sculpture and painting that the civilizations have left us, and we can presume that it is somewhat older, perhaps as old as the cultivation of plants. From studies of these records of past civilizations and of the habits of contemporary man at various stages of cultural development, we can piece together a reasonably probable picture of the evolution of clothing habits.

I have already reviewed the grounds for believing that much of human evolution occurred in or near the tropics, where clothing as protection against weather would be unnecessary. But we also know that man penetrated quite far north in Europe in very early times. There is no reason, however, to assume that these Pleistocene men were addicted to clothes. Naked men are able to survive (and breed) under astonishingly difficult climatic conditions as has been shown, in recent times, by peoples like the Fuegians and the Tasmanians. Darwin's description, in the *Voyage of the Beagle,* of the behavior of the people in the wretched climate of Tierra del Fuego is worth quoting.

"While going one day on shore near Wollaston Island, we pulled alongside a canoe with six Fuegians. These were the most abject and miserable creatures I anywhere beheld. On the East coast the natives, as we have seen, have guanaco cloaks, and on the West, they possess sealskins. Amongst these central tribes the men generally have an otter skin, or some small scrap about as large as a pocket handkerchief, which is barely sufficient to cover their backs as low down as their loins. It is laced across the breast by strings, and according as the wind blows, it is shifted from side to side. But the Fuegians in the canoe were quite naked, and even one full-grown woman was absolutely so. It was raining heavily, and the fresh water, together with the spray, trickled down her body. In another harbor, not far distant, a woman, who was suckling a recently-born child, came one day alongside the vessel, and remained there out of mere curiosity, whilst the sleet fell and thawed on her naked bosom, and on the skin of her naked baby. . . . At night, five or six human beings, naked and scarcely protected from the wind and rain of this tempestuous climate, slept on the wet ground coiled up like animals."

This, it should be remembered, was under midsummer conditions!

The subject of adaptation to cold lies outside the scope of this book, but I might note that a few studies of naked savages in severe climates have indicated differences from Europeans in things like body metabolism and control of skin circulation of blood. These physiological differences probably do not represent racial differences in any inherited sense—more likely they are the result of acclimatization through exposure to severe conditions from birth. To prove this, however, it would be necessary to raise a small group of Europeans, naked and exposed to a comparable environment—an experiment that is unlikely to be carried out.

Certainly clothing and housing were necessary for the penetration of the extreme, arctic environment, and important for ease or comfort under the climatic conditions of Europe, northern Asia and North America. The Eskimos and various Siberian tribes of our own day have clothing habits that appear to be very well adapted to the climate, and the European barbarians described by the Greeks were well-clothed, wearing trouser-like garments.

The clothing worn by contemporary man can be divided into two broad classes: the arctic, based on fitted garments, and especially upon the trouser; and the tropical, based on draped garments, suspended from the waist or the neck. The history of the fitted, arctic garment is obscure because it was not adopted by any civilization until the development of our own Western culture in post-Roman times. Trousers infiltrated the Roman Empire at about the same time as Christianity, though from the opposite direction, and were equally met by scandalized protests and counter legislation. In the sixth and seventh centuries the trousers were concealed under a long coat or cloak, but during the Dark Ages they came out in the open to form the principal male garment; and they have remained, ever since, the most obvious symbol of Westernization. The Western female achieved a compromise between the draped and the fitted clothes types, using sleeves but not (on the outside, at least) trousers. The Muslims, curiously, reversed the sex distinction, since trousers became the distinctive female garment in the Near East.

But our concern with European clothing is limited to its influence in the tropics. Before going into this, it may be interesting to review the varieties of clothing developed by tropical peoples themselves.

Tropical people at the food-gathering stage of culture generally go naked, though they may be addicted to tattooing or body painting. Things like bracelets, anklets, necklaces, ear-plugs and nose-plugs may be adopted at an earlier cultural stage than true clothing, and this seems to indicate a general human tendency to hang such ornaments or charms from any part of the body offering a means of support. The loincloth may have developed, then, from an analogous tendency to attach things to the waist. The sex organs must have become involved in this waist ornamentation at an early period, but not so much for the purpose of concealment as for the opposite, of attracting attention.

Certainly clothing, from the very beginning, serves to reenforce distinctions between the sexes; and as societies become more complex, the details of clothing (however scanty) serve, among the individuals of one sex, to symbolize status. These two functions, the accentuation of sex and the symbolization of status, continue to dominate dress habits in even the most highly developed of cultures, outweighing the secondary functions of modesty and protection. Simple clothing may, however, be retained by quite complex societies; and simple clothing has, indeed, generally characterized the tropical societies, including the tropical civilizations.

We know quite a deal about Mayan dress, from the sculptures and from the descriptions of the first Spaniards. The main garment of the men was the breechclout: a band of cotton cloth the width of the hand, long enough to be wound around the waist several times and passed between the legs to cover the sex organs; one end was left hanging down between the legs in front, the other between the buttocks behind. In addition, the men

Ceremonial Scene from a Mayan Vase, to Show Clothing
(after Morley).

sometimes wore a large square cotton cloth knotted around the shoulders, with decorations indicating the status of the wearer.

According to Bishop Landa, "the women of the coast and of the Provinces of Bacalar and of Campeche are more modest in their dress, for, besides the covering which they wore from the waist down, they covered their breasts, tying a folded cloth underneath their armpits. All of the others did not wear more than one garment like a long and wide sack, opened on both sides, and drawn in as far as the hips, where they fastened it together."

In the ancient oriental civilizations, clothing seems always to have been dominated by considerations of status and caste. In the warmest regions, however, the basic garment of both men and women has long been a cloth wrapper, wound around the waist

or under the armpits, like the *sarongs* of Java. The jacket, now
common in many parts, seems to be a relatively modern addition.

Egypt is technically outside of the tropics but its climate, except for two or three midwinter months, is tropical enough; and
the region is of interest in our present study because we know so
much about its cultural history. Professor Frederick Wulsin has
summarized the dress habits of ancient Egypt as follows:

"A well-to-do man, in the Old Kingdom, wore a white linen
kilt, held above the hips by a belt and reaching to the knee
or calf. Later the kilt grew longer, and an underskirt was added
in Middle Kingdom times. In the New Empire a short shirt,
with or without sleeves, came into fashion; earlier the body
had been bare from the waist up, the chest adorned with a
broad collar, sometimes inlaid with precious stones. The head
was shaven, and covered with a wig on all state occasions. The
feet were usually bare, but sandals of leather or papyrus,
carried by a servant, could be put on when needed. Poorer
men wore a short simple kilt, generally of linen but sometimes
of matting, which was often taken off for hard or dirty work;
sometimes a simple girdle with a fringe was substituted.

"In the Old and Middle Kingdom, women of all classes
wore a thin, close-fitting linen dress, extending from below the
breasts to the ankles, and held up by two braces that passed
over the shoulders like suspenders. It was usually plain, except
for a little embroidery at the top, and was cut very narrow.
Well-to-do ladies wore also a wig, a collar and necklace, and
bracelets. For hard or very active work women of the lower
classes either wore a short skirt or stripped entirely. Serving-
maids at banquets under the Empire are shown wearing only
a broad decorated belt. At the time of the New Empire, a
lady's dress covered the left shoulder but not the right, and
was covered by a cloak pinned on the breast. Both garments
were entirely transparent.

"There is some evidence that the Egyptians shaved the head

and the whole body, yet their medical prescriptions included hair restorers. Apparently as a rule the body and beard were shaved, and the hair worn very short, with a large wig for state occasions, and in addition a false beard for solemn ones. The Egyptians were extremely clean in their persons, given to constant bathing and laundering of clothing. They used oil on the skin, and malachite and galena for eyepaint, besides rouge and other cosmetics, and perfumes."

Of the Sumerians, Wulsin points out that in the early period "people seem to have gone naked or nearly so; at least worshippers are shown approaching the gods without clothing, and there is a sculpture of a fisherman carrying home his catch with only a string around his waist. Later a kilt or skirt of tufted or smooth material came into use, but the upper part of the body was still bare. In many cases the kilt took the form of an apron, split and overlapping in front; and this continued to be the ordinary costume of men and women alike for the whole Sumerian period."

As Wulsin remarks, the Egyptians and the Sumerians created two of the greatest civilizations of which we have knowledge, and "their history points the same lesson: that white men can do hard physical work, and creative intellectual work, in hot countries, and thrive on it. . . . As to dress, we have to note that these ancient peoples wore very little. They were usually bare above the waist, and seem to have stripped entirely when occasion called for it. There is no proof that this is causally connected with the capacity for sustained hard work, which they displayed; but in view of the known effect of clothing in increasing heat load, the theory is tempting."

The whole question of appropriate clothing for the tropics became of great importance to the military forces of the United States during the second world war and various investigations of the subject were sponsored by the Army, the Navy and the Air

Forces. These studies have recently been summarized in a book edited by Dr. L. H. Newburgh, called *Physiology of Heat Regulation and the Science of Clothing*. This is written in a highly technical style (except for Wulsin's introductory chapter from which

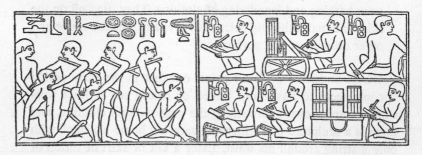

Clothing in Ancient Egypt: Treasury Officers Collecting Taxes
(after Breasted).

I have been quoting), but it contains a vast store of information from which I shall try to extract some pertinent bits.

To understand the relations between man, clothing and climate, we must make a brief excursion into physiology. The temperature and humidity of the external world do not matter to us directly. Our ability to carry out physical work or to think depends on internal factors which control the condition of our muscles or our brain. The proper functioning of these internal organs depends on the various mechanisms for maintaining stable internal bodily conditions—of temperature, blood supply, salt concentrations and so forth. Our feelings of comfort, depression and stimulation then also depend on the way these bodily mechanisms are functioning.

With naked, unreflective man, this might be the whole story. But with man as we know him, these physiological mechanisms are further complicated and modified by clothing, housing, habits and attitudes—the cultural environment again, interposed between physiology and climate. For the moment, however, let's look at the matter in purely physiological terms.

The normal temperature of the internal bodily organs (most easily measured as the rectal temperature) is maintained with considerable constancy at 98.6° F. To maintain this body temperature, heat gain must be balanced by heat loss. To understand the temperature regulation of the body, then, we need to look into two different sets of factors: those that contribute to the warming up of the body, and those that govern the process of cooling off. Let's look first at the sources of body heat.

The three principal sources of body heat are metabolism, convection or conduction (when air temperature is above body temperature), and radiation. The major source is metabolism—the cellular combustion of foodstuffs.

Normal body heat production through metabolism is, of course, the same in the tropics as anywhere else, except for a certain amount of evidence indicating that tropical peoples may have a somewhat lower rate of metabolism than people adapted to cooler climates. The rate of heat production, however, varies greatly with bodily activity. The "average" man at rest produces about 100 calories per hour through normal bodily functions; but this same average man, marching and carrying a pack weighing 65 lbs., will produce 520 calories per hour. Even moderate work, in other words, multiplies heat production five times.

Heat gain by convection or conduction need concern us little, since air temperatures higher than normal body temperature are rarely encountered in the tropics. Heat gain from solar radiation may, however, be important.

The chief source of radiant heat for tropical man is the sun. Sunlight covers a wide spectrum of electromagnetic waves, from the ultraviolet through the visible to far in the infrared. The rays that cause sunburn are in the ultraviolet, below the threshold of visibility. The pigmentation of dark-skinned peoples serves as a protection against the burning effect of these short wave lengths, and some blond people who seem incapable of the "tanning" adaptation to sunlight may be truly and painfully ill-adapted to life in the tropics. In general, though, the relation between pigmentation and protection from damaging ultraviolet is still obscure, because most of the ultraviolet is cut out by the outermost layer of skin, before the pigmentation is reached.

On the good side, it should be mentioned that these ultraviolet rays stimulate vitamin D production, through their action on ergosterol in the deeper skin layers: which makes rickets (caused by vitamin D deficiency) an extremely rare disease in the tropics, except among people who have the custom of protecting their children from sunlight.

Ultraviolet radiation has no heating effect. Heat radiation starts in the visible red and goes far into the infrared. This type of radiation is greatly reduced by air moisture, and radiant heat is thus most important under the dry atmospheric conditions of deserts. It is more a desert than a tropical phenomenon, and most important in the horse latitudes which border on the tropics. The argument for clothes in the tropics is based mostly on the need for protection against radiant heat and becomes thus, really, an argument for clothes under daytime desert conditions.

This has recently become the subject of considerable study because of the exigencies of desert warfare. E. F. Adolph, a scientist working in the Nevada desert, found that a nude man, sitting in the desert sun, gained an average of 143 calories per hour of heat from solar radiation—more heat than that produced by body metabolism in a man resting in the shade. This heat gain could be reduced by half if white clothing was worn. The problem, under these conditions, becomes one of finding clothing that will give protection against heat gain from sunlight, without interference with the air circulation necessary for efficient cooling through the evaporation of sweat.

Paul Siple, in summarizing the observations on clothing and

climate under desert conditions in the volume on the *Physiology of Heat Regulation,* says that "if it were not for the fact that robes or togas have been generally discarded by Western civilization, except for ceremonial indoor usage, a robe worn without underwear would appear to be the best answer for desert clothing. Women's dresses and skirts are basically more suited to desert wear than trousers. The next best approach would seem to be the use of a short, loose jacket and loose trousers suspended rather than belted. By being kept loose, these garments should have some of the benefits of the robe."

Under most tropical conditions, heat gain from solar radiation is no more important than it is under summer conditions in the north because the infrared rays are screened out by atmospheric moisture. The primary problem, in designing tropical clothing, is not to provide protection from heat gain through radiation, but to avoid interference with heat loss through sweating. This brings us to the general question of the ways in which the body keeps cool: the mechanisms for heat loss.

Physiologists recognize six mechanisms for heat loss from the body: 1, radiation, convection and conduction; 2, evaporation of sweat; 3, vaporization of water from lungs; 4, liberation of dissolved carbon dioxide in the lungs; 5, the warming of inspired air; and 6, through urine and faeces. Of these, the first two are overwhelmingly important, accounting for more than 80 per cent of the body's heat loss; and it is these two, precisely, that have the greatest dependence on climatic conditions, and that are drastically modified by the nature of clothing.

Where the air temperature is considerably below body temperature, radiation and convection form the chief means of heat loss, but as air temperatures approach normal body temperature, the sweat mechanism becomes increasingly important until, when the two temperatures are equal, or the air temperature higher, the radiation mechanism becomes inoperative, or becomes a factor in heat gain rather than heat loss.

The human skin is an extremely good radiator of heat, behaving very like the ideal "black body" of radiation equations, and in a cool climate the heat generated by body metabolism and by work is almost all dissipated by radiation. In my day it was a common trick of elementary physics to show how the heat radiated by a man could be detected across the room with a thermocouple. This efficient radiation behavior seems odd at first, because the skin of a European, at least, doesn't look like an ideal "black body." But radiation efficiency involves the infrared, invisible portion of the spectrum; and in this region the skin of all men is "black," that is, completely absorptive. The emissive power of an object, in radiation, is directly proportional to its absorbing power, and inversely proportional to its reflecting power. Thus, the skin reflects no heat, but absorbs heat radiated to it, and radiates heat brought to the surface from the interior of the body.

Radiation accounts for most of the body's heat loss in resting, unclothed men, until the air temperature gets above 88° F. (31° C.), when the sweat mechanism starts to operate. Sweating starts, of course, at lower temperatures if body heat is raised through work, or the radiation mechanism blanketed with clothes —the precise temperature depending on the nature and amount of work or clothing. The rate at which the sweat evaporates depends on the air humidity, the air temperature and air circulation. With hot, dry, well-ventilated conditions, sweat may hardly be perceptible even though the body is pouring it out; while in a warm, moist and still environment—under muggy conditions— the whole skin surface is soon wet, and the excess starts dripping off the nose and chin.

Under extreme conditions of heat and work, like those that may prevail in the boiler room of a ship, the body may produce astonishing quantities of sweat. Rates above two quarts an hour have commonly been reported, and for short periods sweat production may even reach a rate of four quarts an hour. These records, it should be emphasized, are based on laboratory studies under severe conditions, of a sort unlikely to be encountered by the ordinary person in the tropics or anywhere else. Something between a pint and a quart of sweat per hour, however, may be produced to control body temperature under conditions like that of brisk walking in the humid, lowland tropics, and this can add up to a considerable amount of water and salt loss during the day.

Obviously, it is reasonable to drink plenty of water under humid, tropical conditions; and extra salt may be advisable. Sweat ordinarily contains between 0.2 and 0.5 per cent of salt. The amount varies greatly among individuals, but in general it is lowest in people who have become acclimatized to tropical conditions. Salt tablets, then, are particularly advisable for newcomers, and for people engaged in heavy, muscular work.

The whole bodily system for heat control is extraordinarily adaptable. This is fortunate for man, since it enables him to get along in all sorts of different climates; but it makes experimentation and description difficult. Some changes are quite rapid. The amount of salt in sweat, for instance, drops within a week or two of residence in a muggy climate, and various other changes occur which result in more efficient control of body temperature. Other adaptations are much slower, and there is some evidence that environmental conditions during the growing period of childhood may influence the number and distribution of sweat glands in the skin.

When the system for bodily heat control fails to function in a hot environment, acute illness results. The word "sunstroke" faded out of the medical literature many years ago, as it was realized that acute effects were due, not to the direct action of the sun, but to the failure of bodily temperature control. Three varieties of acute heat effects are now generally recognized: heat cramps, heat exhaustion and heat stroke.

Heat cramps, or stoker's cramps, are characterized by the

development of painful muscular cramps following exertion in high temperatures. The onset is usually gradual, with mild cramps in the arms and legs, which recur at increasingly short intervals and with increasing severity, finally involving the muscles of the abdominal wall. The cramps are caused by depletion of the body's salt content through profuse sweating, and treatment consists in giving salt tablets and lots of water. In severe cases, normal salt solution is injected intravenously.

Heat exhaustion is a generalized response to prolonged exposure to high temperature, caused by a breakdown in the efficiency of the blood circulation. The first symptoms may be a vague malaise, headache, irritability, nausea, and so forth. The blood pressure and pulse pressure fall, and there is profuse sweating, with a cold, clammy skin. The treatment is for acute circulatory failure.

Heat stroke is caused by an acute failure of the heat control mechanism, usually resulting from prolonged exposure to very high temperatures accompanied by high humidity and lack of air movement; heavy physical work, tight clothing, and alcohol may be influential. Cessation of sweating may occur some time in advance of the acute attack, providing a warning signal. With the onset of the "stroke" there is vomiting, pericardial distress, muscular twitchings, and a rapid rise in body temperature with delirium, followed by coma. Treatment involves immediate attempts to reduce the body temperature—things like cold sponges, wet packs and continuous fanning.

I got off on this subject of acute disease resulting from heat because it seemed a logical extension of the discussion of heat control mechanisms. But I want to emphasize again that none of these three conditions is particularly characteristic of the tropics. In fact, if statistics were available, we would probably find such conditions to be more common in the American midwest during the summer than anywhere in the equatorial regions. For more characteristically tropical effects of maladjustment to heat, we should turn to conditions that result from prolonged and continuous exposure to a warm, humid climate. Two quite different sorts of things deserve consideration in this connection: specific skin disorders, like "prickly heat," and the general debility or lassitude that is alleged to result from tropical residence.

I plan to devote a separate chapter to tropical diseases, and skin disorders might appropriately be taken up in that connection. But the term tropical diseases calls to mind things like malaria, yellow fever and sleeping sickness which are predominantly tropical because the tropical environment is especially favorable for the life cycle of the causative parasite, not because of any direct effect of climate on man. Many of the tropical skin troubles involve parasites—especially fungi—but I suspect that these parasites are often secondary; that the primary difficulty involves skin adjustments to climate (and to clothing).

My feeling about this is based partly on my experience with the staff of the yellow fever laboratory at Villavicencio. The technicians—men employed locally—were constantly plagued with the disease called "athlete's foot," as so many people are in the tropics. They experimented with all kinds of fungicidal treatments which were recommended by the local doctors, or which they thought up themselves, but with very indifferent results.

It seemed to me probable that the trouble was caused by the fact that they had taken to wearing shoes and socks. The "common people" of the region went barefooted, or wore light canvas sandals called *alpargates*; but these men, proud of their status as technicians in the laboratory, had adopted the shoes which were the local equivalent of white collars. I wore sandals, since I was not worried about my status and never felt comfortable in shoes anyway, and I had no trouble with my feet. I finally managed to persuade the staff also to abandon shoes, except for ceremonial occasions, and with this shift, athlete's foot ceased to be a problem in the laboratory.

I was pleased to find in the Newburgh book on the *Physiology of Heat Regulation* the statement that "Lt. Colonel Lawrence Irving, AAF, and his colleagues at Eglin Field, Florida, showed conclusively that ventilation of the feet obtained by wearing sandals will prevent as well as cure fungus infections of the feet which are so prevalent in hot climates. This is a practical procedure for all personnel in the tropics except the soldier in actual combat, and even then he might make some use of the idea."

But to realize the cultural difficulties, it is only necessary to stop and think for a moment about the idea of putting the American army, on tropical service, in sandals! An army without boots to polish is unthinkable, and to hell with the climate.

As Paul Siple points out, later in the same book: "It is evident that clothing designed for tropical wear is not basically for thermal protection. Clothing worn for the sake of convention, ornamentation, or protection against other environmental factors inhibits optimum efficiency for body cooling and adds to heat stress. The clothing problem for this zone resolves itself in a compromise between providing the ideal of no clothing, and furnishing a satisfactory covering to meet purely psychological and physical needs."

Prickly heat, again, is to be blamed directly on clothing draped over a sweating skin, sometimes aggravated by an overly enthusiastic use of soap. The heat rash itself is bad enough, but in addition the disturbed skin makes a splendid growing medium for all kinds of micro-organisms, and the end result may be very messy indeed.

My second category of climate effects, tropical debility or lassitude, involves the whole question of physiological and psychological adjustments to tropical conditions. On the subject of climate and physiology, there is a very extensive literature, reviewing endless experiments with treadmills and hot rooms and cold rooms and mental efficiency and rectal temperature, replete with graphs, tables and mathematical equations. Unfortunately, it seems to add up to a demonstration that the experimental approach to this kind of a problem is difficult.

Alongside this experimental material is the even wordier accumulation of observations and deductions and verbalizations of prejudice on the general subject of the course of human events in relation to the climatic pattern of the globe—on climate and psychology.

Our interest in the matter centers on the adaptability of the white, or European, races to the tropics, and on the reasons for their failure to make a very good showing in the equatorial regions. Perhaps, then, we can appropriately twist the meaning of a common catch-phrase, and discuss the question under the heading of "the white man's burden."

CHAPTER VIII

★

The White Man's Burden

AS far as I can remember, I didn't have any particular theory in mind about man or civilization in the tropics when I started to write this book. I wanted to describe the tropical region as I knew it: a pleasant place to live and work, full of interesting plants, interesting animals, interesting people, abounding in problems for the biologist which were largely neglected because most biologists live in the north, making only rare and periodic excursions into this fascinating equatorial environment. A theory, however, has gradually formed as I have got on with the job of gathering and organizing the material for the book and writing it out in chapter form.

This theory is that the white man's burden in the tropics is not the burden of educating, improving, or governing the poor benighted natives; it is the burden of his own culture which he has carried into an alien environment.

There is a row of books on the desk in front of me, each of which develops at more or less length, and with more or less scholarly documentation, the theory that the tropical regions are unfavorable for civilization. I'll list the more important of these in my bibliography, though with the hope that such listing will not constitute any useful advertisement for the books in question. The best known, the classic, of the series is Ellsworth Hunting-

118

ton's *Civilization and Climate*; and I have gradually come to think of my own book as my "anti-Huntington tract." Huntington is dead now, so I cannot convince him of the error of his ways, nor elicit any reply. But he has many disciples who are very much alive, and some quite handy with the typewriter, so my present position is no mere exercise in shadow-boxing.

The basic mistake of the climate-and-civilization people, it seems to me, lies in confusing "civilization" with "Western civilization." The anthropologists call this being "ethnocentric"; and apparently all cultures tend to be ethnocentric, to regard their own ways as good and other ways as bad, except where considerations of obvious utility, prestige or something of that sort complicate the picture. The recognition and emphasis of this concept of ethnocentricity is, I think, one of the major contributions of anthropology to human thought.

The ethnocentric point of view is illustrated by the way the Jews called themselves *the* chosen people; by the Greek attitude toward "barbarians"; and by our own behavior toward non-Western peoples whom we lump as "natives." As Arnold Toynbee says, "when we Westerners call people 'natives' we implicitly take the cultural colour out of our perception of them. We see them as wild animals infesting the country in which we happen to come across them, as part of the local flora and fauna and not as men of like passions with ourselves. So long as we think of them as 'natives' we may exterminate them or, as is more likely today, domesticate them and honestly (perhaps not altogether mistakenly) believe that we are improving the breed, but we do not begin to understand them."

Another source of confusion in Western thinking is what Toynbee calls "the thesis of the unity of civilization." This, he says, "is a misconception into which modern Western historians have been led by the influence of their social environment. The misleading feature is the fact that, in modern times, our own Western civilization has cast the net of its economic system all round the World, and this economic unification on a Western basis has been followed by a political unification on the same basis that has gone almost as far; for though the conquests of Western armies and governments have been neither as extensive nor as thorough as the conquests of Western manufacturers and technicians, it is nevertheless a fact that all of the states of the contemporary world form part of a single political system of Western origin."

He points out that "while the economic and political maps have now been Westernized, the cultural map remains substantially what it was before our Western Society started on its career of economic and political conquest."

That Western culture is not well adapted to the tropical environment, I will readily admit, though the modifications necessary for adaptation may not be very profound. Our civilization has its roots in the Mediterranean cultures, but its modern development has mostly occurred north of the Alps, in central and western Europe, in regions characterized by strong seasonal temperature changes. This northward spread of civilized culture did not occur until late Roman times and it depended, I think, on cultural inventions enabling man to overcome the climatic environment, especially on the development of methods of housing, heating, lighting and clothing.

In other words, the western European environment, lauded by Ellsworth Huntington and his followers as ideal for the development of civilization, was an insurmountable obstacle to civilization until methods had been found for mitigating its effects. The progress of human culture requires the development of thought. And surely reflective thinking requires a modicum of comfort, in the sense of freedom from physical misery; and of leisure, at least for the thinkers if not for the whole society. Leisure and freedom from physical misery are easy to come by in many parts of the tropics and adjacent lands; and they may be possible during the brief months of the northern summer. But winter is something else. How could any very "high" level of culture develop among ill-clad people, huddled over the open fires of smoke-filled, drafty huts? There may be leisure, if food supplies have been stored, but it is hardly of a thought-provoking sort; and comfort is unknown.

As S. F. Markham has pointed out, "it was three innovations, the chimney, the grate, and the use of coal, combined with new developments in architecture, which changed the whole history of mankind." Unfortunately, little is known about the early history of the hearth and chimney, though the earliest known chimney pieces date from the 12th century. The spread of more efficient methods of building, heating and lighting—and artificial lighting is necessary for much reading or writing during the northern winter—coincided with the rise of Western civilization in Europe after the 13th century, and it can be plausibly argued that these developments, leading to the control of the unfavorable climate, were a prime cause of that civilization.

It has been argued from this that further development of civilization in the tropics will depend on an analogous development, in the spread of air conditioning. Under extreme conditions of heat and humidity, this may be true. But over much of the tropics, I suspect that air conditioning contributes to comfort because people are wearing clothes and living in houses that are ill-adapted to the climate. It seems to me a sad commentary on human nature and on the persistence of cultural traits, that we find it easier to plan elaborate and expensive modification of the indoor climate, so that we can continue to wear arctic-type garments, than to contemplate exchanging those garments for types better suited to local conditions.

The situation with regard to clothes is readily recognized and described. But I suspect that the clothes are an obvious symbol of many less easily recognized cultural traits that we carry from the north into the tropics and that, in more subtle ways, are the cause of maladjustment, of tropical lassitude, of the "deterioration of white men in the tropics" and that, in their sum, constitute the "white man's burden."

Take the matter of climate and energy. A cold climate is certainly stimulating in the sense that activity is necessary for bodily functioning, that you will freeze to death if you don't keep moving. Perhaps this situation has led Western culture to place an especial value on mere activity. We tend, I think, to confuse activity with accomplishment, and to consider "being busy" a virtue in itself.

A warm climate, on the other hand, offers no such obvious stimulus to physical activity, and an excess of activity in fact places an extra load on the body cooling mechanism. This may, in the long run, influence the orientation of cultures, leading warm-climate civilizations to place greater emphasis on contemplation and philosophy, to prize spiritual rather than material values. At least the great religions of mankind have mostly arisen among warm-climate cultures, while industrialization is the product of the cold-climate West.

Nowadays, to be sure, the tropical peoples are all anxious to adopt the industrialization process, just as, in the past, northern peoples have adopted and spread the southern religions, so that my generalization is not a very clear-cut affair. Perhaps the most that should be said is that different environments influence the development of different value systems and that climate, in this process, may be an important environmental influence.

The relationships between culture and climate are almost inextricably mixed up with those between race and climate. I say "almost" because I think it should be possible to untangle the two, even though I don't think this has yet been done. This is most apparent in the large literature on "the white man in the tropics" in which the physiological characteristics of European man are very generally confused with the psychological and cultural traits of Western civilization.

The work on racial differences in relation to climate is especially disappointing, and it turns out that this is a very difficult subject on which to design clear-cut experiments. I remember discussing the matter with a scientist who had been carrying out studies of Europeans and natives in Africa. He found various differences in performance under carefully standardized conditions, and I asked whether these differences might not be due to things like differences in nutrition, or to past and present diseases. He readily admitted that such factors had not been ruled out, but said that his object was to compare Europeans and Africans as he found them, not as they might be under some hypothetical, ideal conditions. This sort of study is important, all right, for various practical purposes, but it has little relevance to the intriguing problem of what are the inherent physiological differences among human races.

Some of the best work has been carried out in the southern United States, using whites and negroes of similar economic and social background, and these studies have not revealed any clear-cut difference in things like capacity for physical work, control of body temperature under conditions of stress, or such-like measurable factors. The whole subject, I think, warrants much more careful study than it has yet received.

The matter of race, climate and intelligence seems also to be something about which we are remarkably ignorant. I suppose the key problem here is the nature of "intelligence." When we use the word, we mean innate or inherited differences in mental capacities or aptitudes. We are sure that such differences exist among individuals, and it seems perfectly logical that there should be statistical or average differences among large groups of people, such as geographically separated races. But we seem to have made extraordinarily little progress in finding ways of describing and measuring such capacities and aptitudes.

Again culture seems to provide the confusing factor. Such progress as we have made in isolating aptitudes, measuring "intelligence quotients" and describing personality types is limited to comparisons within a single culture, our own. The limitations of our methods are nicely shown by the comparative studies that have been made in the United States between southerners and northerners, negroes and whites. With such studies, one can show that in the United States, whites have higher I.Q.s than negroes; that northerners have higher I.Q.s than southerners. Such data have been used to demonstrate, on the one hand, that climate influences intelligence; or on the other hand, that there are racial differences in intelligence. Any particular theory can be supported by selecting the right data. People who want to demolish the racial theory, for instance, point out that negroes from certain northern states have higher I.Q.s than whites from certain southern states, and so forth.

The actual correlation, in the case of these group differences in average I.Q. is, of course, with the availability and quality of educational opportunity: which shows that these tests are not measuring inherent intelligence, but general cultural level. Individual differences in I.Q. among people with the same cultural background and educational opportunities are something else again. In such cases, where the cultural factors are constant, we seem to be measuring a reflection of inherent differences, which may very well have a genetic origin. But we have not yet devised a sure way of demonstrating such differences among individuals or groups with diverging cultural and educational backgrounds.

When it comes to making comparisons among peoples with different linguistic backgrounds, we find even greater difficulties. The way we think, and the kind of discriminations that we make, is very much bound up with the structure of our language, and different languages have very different structures.

In the southern-northern comparisons in the United States, the climate people of course maintain that the backward educational systems of the south are a reflection of the unfavorable climate of that region, so that the I.Q. differences are still correlated with climate, even though indirectly. My feeling is that the relative backwardness of the south reflects some general phenomenon of cultural drift with complex causation; and that climate enters into this causation, if at all, very indirectly through obscure factors of cultural maladjustment.

If the correlation were direct, with temperature and latitude, Florida should be at the bottom of the list, which it isn't. Ellsworth Huntington, somewhere, uses the backwardness of North Carolina as an example of the effect of unfortunate climatic conditions. Yet between the time he wrote and the time I am writing, North Carolina ruined his argument by forging ahead into a position of relative leadership. California was the most backward part of North America when the continent was inhabited exclusively by Indians. Now that the palefaces have taken over, California has been called many things, but not backward. Yet the climate, for North Carolina or California, has undergone no detectable change.

If, then, we cannot make any clear or valid deductions about race, climate and intelligence within the United States, I would regard inquiry into conditions in Abyssinia, Java, Venezuela and Siam as quite futile. Futile probably isn't the word, because the inquiry would certainly be important from the point of view of gaining understanding of human behavior. "Unrewarding" would probably be a better word, because we just haven't got the kind of data on which valid conclusions could be based; perhaps we haven't even found the right approach or method for making such studies.

Our ignorance about intelligence becomes less surprising when we discover our ignorance about other more obvious and more easily measurable differences among people of different races living in different climates. I started to look up material on age at puberty, for instance, since this is one of the things that is usually supposed to vary with race and climate. I got discouraged, though, by finding completely conflicting opinions as to whether onset of sexual maturity was earlier or later in the tropics than in colder climates. There probably are good data on this somewhere, but I haven't come across usable summaries.

Or take the matter of extent and nature of sexual activity. The tropics are generally supposed to stimulate sexual activity and sexual desire, and tropical peoples are generally alleged to be a pretty sexual bunch. Europeans in the tropics certainly often show sexual behavior patterns that are different from those presumed to be followed in Europe, but I suspect that this is the result, not of the climate, but of being away from home. Sexual behavior is so strictly conditioned by cultural patterns, that I would expect any racial or climatic influence to be very difficult indeed to demonstrate. Some tropical peoples have elaborate restrictive taboos on intercourse, and the idea of celibacy seems to be a tropical, or at least southern, invention. The Eskimos, on the other hand, are said to carry on scandalously in their igloos all winter long, having nothing else much to do.

Our knowledge of the influence of race and climate upon energy, upon intelligence, and upon sexual behavior seems, then, to be inadequate for the formulation of any very broad or sound generalizations about Europeans in the tropics. Before leaving this general subject, we might look at one other topic, that of race, climate and disease. I plan to devote the next chapter to tropical diseases, but from the rather special point of view of describing the transmission mechanisms of some of the more notorious infections. This is different from our present interest, which turns on the question of racial immunity and the general influence of climate and culture.

The lowland tropics have long been noted as unhealthful, especially for Europeans. Tropical Africa, during the whole period of European exploitation, has been famous as the "white man's grave," and the statistics on mortality and morbidity among soldiers, officials and traders show that this epithet has been well justified.

All through the 19th century, a yearly death rate of 10 per

cent among European officials in West Africa was not unusual, and a death rate of 5 per cent was considered favorable. This, it must be remembered, involved mostly people between the ages of 18 and 50, who had passed physical examinations before leaving home. This death rate dropped rapidly around the turn of the century. The average death rate for European officials on the Gold Coast between 1881 and 1897 was 76 per thousand; in 1902 it was 31 per thousand; in 1903, 22 per thousand; and in 1904, 13 per thousand; and since 1925 it has never been above 10 per thousand. This is about the same as the average death rate in the United States. But the comparison is unfair, since in West Africa we are dealing with a selected population in the prime of life, who ought to have a very low death rate indeed.

The Spaniards in tropical America placed most of their capitals in the cool mountain uplands—Mexico City is 7,400 feet above the sea level; Guatemala City, 5,000 feet; San Jose, Costa Rica, 3,900 feet; Bogotá, Colombia, 8,600 feet; Caracas, Venezuela, 3,000 feet; Quito, Ecuador, 9,300 feet. These sites were selected partly for protection against pirates and invaders; partly because Spaniards found the cool uplands more homelike than the warm lowlands; partly because they found important Indian cities already located there; but also because they soon found by experience that these mountain locations were more healthful. These mountain Spaniards have long continued to dread the lowlands of their own countries. Our friends in Bogotá, I remember, were horrified at the idea of our living and raising our children in the lowland town of Villavicencio. And in Guatemala, the railway found it advisable to arrange schedules so that travelers could go directly from the boat train to the steamer, because the city people were afraid to spend a night in the port.

In short, the lowland tropics have long had a bad reputation from the point of view of health—a reputation that is pretty well justified by the statistics and by the experience of European settlers. Our present task is to examine this situation from the point of view of influence of climate, culture and racial susceptibility.

Disease is a very broad word, covering any impairment of bodily or mental well-being. We have gradually got different categories of disease sorted out according to kind of causation: diseases resulting from infection with parasitic organisms; diseases resulting from food deficiencies; diseases resulting from congenital defects; psychosomatic diseases, resulting from mental disturbances of one sort or another, and so forth. All of these various sorts of diseases have probably entered into the problems of Europeans in the tropics, and any adequate examination of the matter would require book-length treatment in itself.

The parasitic diseases of the tropics are numerous, important, and in part distinctive; they are commonly considered to be the greatest hazard of life in the lowland tropics, and I plan to discuss some of them in the next chapter. Medical science has been particularly successful with these diseases, and we now know enough to make the lowland tropics as free from infectious disease as any other part of the world. The application of this knowledge is something else again—it would require economic, political and cultural changes that are beyond the competence of medicine, or perhaps of any present planned manipulation. That they can occur, however, is a matter of historical record. Europe in the fifteenth and sixteenth centuries was as unhealthy as any region in the tropics today and this should give us pause in making any sweeping generalizations about geography, climate and disease. When we make comparisons in morbidity and mortality between sixteenth century England and twentieth century England, we don't drag in the unhealthful climate; yet as far as I can see, the comparison between 16th and 20th century England is essentially a similar process to comparison between 20th century Burma and 20th century England.

But the European, of course, found things different when he

moved from England to Burma, whether he did this in the 16th century or in the 20th. Which brings in the question of race, and susceptibility and immunity to infectious disease.

The infectious disease picture of the world changed radically in the 16th century, when the explosion of Western civilization scattered and thoroughly mixed most of man's common parasites. Things like smallpox and measles caused havoc in large populations where these diseases had never been encountered before. I cannot prove it, but I believe that the Europeans and their slaves brought malaria and yellow fever to America and carried back syphilis to Europe in exchange.

A new parasite, in each such case, caused havoc among susceptible populations until some sort of an equilibrium was established. I don't think we fully understand how such equilibria become established (or how they sometimes get upset again in periodic epidemic conditions) but the process is probably complex, involving influences on both the parasites and the hosts. Perhaps people with a heredity that makes them especially susceptible to some particular disease get eliminated, so that the descendants of the survivors represent a more resistant population. This may have happened with measles among the Polynesians. Sometimes the parasite seems to become less virulent with time, as perhaps happened with syphilis among Europeans. Most commonly, after a new disease becomes endemic in a population, there is a shift in the age-group attacked, so that people acquire a complete or partial immunity in childhood.

A disease that attacks mostly children is a much less obvious hazard for the population as a whole. For one thing, some diseases appear to be less virulent in children than in adults, as seems to be the case with measles, mumps and perhaps poliomyelitis among our own contemporary diseases. For another thing, infant mortality, in most human cultures, is very high; and deaths from particular diseases are swamped in the general large number of infant deaths, which may mostly appear to be caused by various colics and dysenteries. Our attention is attracted to the occasional adult who, surviving the accidents of childhood, is stricken by this particular disease.

I suspect that this difference in age incidence accounts for much of the supposed European racial susceptibility to tropical disease. In tropical Africa, for instance, most of the local people get yellow fever in childhood. There is some evidence that the disease may be less severe then, and certainly the children who have been infected and have survived are then immune for life. Europeans, coming into this environment, carried with them no childhood immunity; and the mortality among Europeans as compared with the local adults was striking indeed. Malaria is different, since there is no lasting immunity. But where a population is saturated with malaria from childhood, the surviving adults seem to have built up a sort of tolerance of the local parasite strains, so that while they could not be called "healthy," they at least are not stricken with the dramatic severity of new-coming Europeans.

There may well be some racial differences among men in susceptibility to disease. Anyone who has carried out much laboratory work with infections of rats and mice is impressed by the great differences in susceptibility among different strains, and the same thing could well happen with men. But it is very difficult to prove. Perhaps the most frequently cited instance is that of the racial difference between whites and negroes in the United States in susceptibility to tuberculosis. But I have never seen any data in which it seemed to me that the economic and cultural factors had been ruled out. We know that tuberculosis is especially related to bad diet, bad housing, bad medical care; and it seems perfectly possible that the higher incidence of T.B. among negroes is related to this, rather than to any direct racial factor.

I can cite one instance of racial differences in the tropics from my own experience. Europeans coming into the tropics often complain vociferously (and not without reason) about the bites of insects, and noticing the relative calm of the local people, assume that they are much less bothered. I had occasion to carry out a long series of experiments with different insect repellents, testing them on a variety of different people for protection against blackflies and mosquitoes. I also tested the same people without repellents, to find out how they differed in attractiveness for these insects.

It turned out that different people differed greatly in the number of blackflies and mosquitoes that would come to bite them. For the most part, there seemed to be no rhyme or reason about this. A would always be bitten by twice as many mosquitoes as B, B by more than C, and so forth, and I never found any clear-cut explanation. But in general, the darker the skin color, the more bites. Invariably, when there was a negro and a paleface in the same experiment, the negro got the most bites. Color wasn't the whole explanation, because two people with the same skin color might also differ consistently in number of bites; but color as a factor could at least be demonstrated in the laboratory because if a man covered his hand with a glove which was half white and half black, and stuck it in a cage full of hungry mosquitoes, the mosquitoes would mostly settle on the black half. The relatively dark skin of tropical peoples seems to be definitely disadvantageous, then, as far as attractiveness to biting insects is concerned.

I might note that the fact that local people do not seem to be bothered as much by insect bites as newcomers are, is probably a matter of acquired immunity. We have found often enough, in feeding laboratory mosquitoes, that a given person of whatever race can build up an immunity to the toxic effects of the bite of a particular kind of mosquito through frequent exposure— though this immunity is never complete.

The problem of the white man in the tropics involves, of course, much more than racial and cultural adaptation to the climatic environment. The European is almost never alone in the tropics—he is in contact with other races and other cultures, and these contacts give rise to a whole series of special effects that are often blamed on the climate.

The average European (or North American) for the last several hundred years has been convinced that he belonged to a superior race and a superior culture, and during most of that time he has been able to back up this feeling of superiority by force of arms and by adroit manipulation of economic and political forces. The arms, economics and politics have begun to backfire, and the Westerner's superiority is rapidly becoming complicated by frustration and bewilderment.

In individual terms, the problems of the European intruder in tropical cultures can often be ascribed to a change in status. The housewife, accustomed to looking after her own house and family, finds herself with a staff of servants, but with no cultural conditioning for a life of leisure. Her energies, then, go into bridge, gossip, complaints about the stupidity of native cooks and maids, cocktail parties and suchlike things, which often lead to a whole set of psychological and physiological troubles familiar enough to every manager of foreign enterprises in the tropics. The man finds parallel changes in status—the mechanic, clerk, and petty executive finds himself in a position of power out of all proportion to anything he would enjoy in his own culture; and this power, like power everywhere, starts its corrupting influence.

Grenfell Price, in his admirable book on *White Settlers in the Tropics,* found that the most successful settlements were those in which the members of the white community were actively involved in carrying out the physical work of the community. He came to the conclusion, not that physical work was deleterious in the tropics, but that it was essential for health. The trouble is that in most places the white men are so preoccupied with maintaining their dignity and prestige that they leave all opportunities for healthful work to the natives, ending up themselves with cirrhosis of the liver.

In general, wherever Europeans and indigenous peoples live in close contact in the tropics, the indigenous peoples certainly seem to be, biologically, more successful. But this racial juxtaposition also involves a cultural juxtaposition, and the juxtaposition serves to reenforce the cultural differences. The European is determined to preserve what he can of his way of life, and he scorns and ostracizes his fellows who "go native." That means that he clings to a European-type dress, European-type diet, European-type housing, all of which are probably far less suited to local conditions than the corresponding native types. He refuses to "lower" his standards, and as a result he cannot compete with the native on equal terms. But this inability to compete is *cultural,* not biological.

I am not saying that I think Europeans ought to adopt African tribal customs, or wrap sarongs about their waists and start tapping rubber trees in Indonesia. But I think they ought to stop talking about their superior race and superior culture, and stop being preoccupied with maintaining their superior status as minorities in alien environments. To go back to my starting point in this chapter, I think their real burden while living in the tropics is the load of their own civilization. This load contains some articles of real and demonstrable value, particularly among the sciences and technologies; but it also contains a lot of plain rubbish that would better long since have been thrown away.

CHAPTER IX

★

Tropical Diseases

OST people, when they think of the tropics, think also of disease. The average traveler, starting out for any place south of the line of Cancer, gets a collection of "shots" from his doctor, along with the visas from the consulates and the tickets from the steamship line. The connection is made closer by the fact that the consulates and the steamship lines usually require certificates of vaccination against this and that as part of the essential documentation for the trip.

Books and articles giving advice about the tropics always dedicate a good deal of space to disease. They recommend the avoidance of salads and other raw foods. They warn about the danger of drinking water, though they are even more explicit about the danger of alcoholic beverages, and end by recommending water plus some disinfectant or other. They stress the importance of staying under a mosquito bar after nightfall, and they may recommend a whole list of prophylactics against this and preventives for that. I often wonder that anyone ventures into the tropics after reading one of these compilations of advice.

The popular books, however, are relatively mild. For real discouragement, the prospective traveler should consult a textbook of tropical medicine. These are replete with gruesome photographs of people with noses eaten away by yaws, of the

134

colorful ulcerations of cutaneous leishmaniasis (oriental sore), of the multifarious manifestations of skin fungus infections. Leprosy is usually well illustrated, and there may be color plates of different kinds of skin rashes, useful in differentiating tropical fevers. And then there is, of course, always the photograph of some victim of filariasis carrying his testicles in a wheelbarrow (or at least sufficiently enlarged so that a wheelbarrow would seem a convenience if available).

I shall not try to debunk this concept of tropical disease, because goodness knows the diseases are real enough and prevalent enough over wide tropical areas. The lay reader, thumbing through a textbook, gets a misleading impression, of course, since the illustrations mostly represent extremes, selected because these show most clearly the differential characteristics of various diseases. A textbook of diseases current in New York City can be equally horrifying, though the labels under the pictures will have less exotic explanatory material. The problem with tropical disease is not to minimize its importance, but to give it proper perspective in relation to the disease problems of man as a whole.

Disease, even with this perspective, still has a peculiar importance in the tropics. For one thing, there are more different kinds of diseases in the tropics than anywhere else. This reflects the general profusion of tropical nature, which I hope to discuss in later chapters. The tropics have more kinds of flowers, more kinds of trees, more kinds of birds than the higher latitudes; so also they have more kinds of parasites, which in turn are capable of causing more kinds of disease. This does not necessarily mean a greater amount of sickness. A forest composed of one kind of tree may be just as dense as a forest made up of dozens of kinds; or a plague of one disease, like tuberculosis, may cause as much sickness and misery in a northern city as a dozen different diseases in a tropical city.

For another thing, modern medicine is a product of Western civilization, and it has been most effective within the cultural context of that civilization—which means, for the most part, in non-tropical areas. In other words, disease conditions in the tropics are in part dependent on the cultural environment rather than the climatic environment. Diseases that we now think of as primarily tropical were once much more widely spread. Malaria, for instance, was common a hundred years ago in places like Denmark, Sweden, England, Connecticut and Michigan. Bubonic plague was one of the diseases that swept across medieval Europe with disastrous effect. Yellow fever invaded New Orleans periodically, and was the cause of a great epidemic in Philadelphia.

I lived for four years in Albania, which lies in the latitude of New York. The disease picture in Albania, however, was essentially similar to that of many tropical countries, and probably like that of all of Europe a few centuries ago. I do not think medicine, or sanitation as such, deserves all of the credit for the change of conditions. Much must be a result of general economic and cultural factors which have led to the present Western "standards of living" and which have often resulted in the disappearance of disease without any conscious medical intervention.

Probably tropical medicine ought to mean the study of disease conditions, of whatever sort, in relation to tropical environmental conditions. But tropical conditions, both climatic and cultural, are so diverse that this would be practically synonymous with medicine as a whole. If we look at the actual contents of the textbooks, or the subjects of study in institutes of tropical medicine, we find nothing of the sort. Mostly they deal with a rather long list of specific parasitic diseases that are not now common in the West: yellow fever, malaria, typhus, leprosy, plague, yaws, amoebic and other dysenteries, intestinal worms, sleeping sickness and so on.

The concentration of tropical medicine on this list of specific diseases reflects the fact that they are all diseases rather difficult to study in modern Western nations because of their rarity. Consequently institutes with special facilities have to be set up to work on them. The famous schools and institutes of tropical medicine are mostly in the great seaports, like Hamburg, Liverpool and London, where sailors and other visitors to foreign parts, coming back with special diseases, would be available for study. Also much of the work on tropical medicine has been fostered by the Western colonial governments, which have been interested in the special disease conditions encountered by their colonial administrators. Tropical countries themselves would be unlikely to sort out half of the local diseases for special study under some label like "tropical medicine" and leave the other half for study under some other label like "general medicine."

Whatever the historical reasons for the listing of certain diseases as "tropical," it turns out that any such list includes an unusual number of diseases caused by parasites with complicated life histories. Much of the research in tropical medicine has thus been concerned with the investigation of insects as vectors of disease, and with the study of the development of a wide variety of parasites.

The study of insects as vectors of disease started with Patrick Manson, who has been called "the father of tropical medicine." Manson was the first scientist to demonstrate that a particular insect was the transmitting agent for a particular disease. Before his time, local peoples had occasionally noticed the relation between diseases and certain insects, sometimes rightly as in the case of the African tribes that attributed sleeping sickness to the tsetse fly. And in the scientific literature, earlier suggestions can be found of the possible relation between biting insects and disease, especially with regard to malaria and yellow fever. But there was no experimental evidence.

Manson got interested in elephantiasis while stationed at Amoy, on the south China coast. Others had already demonstrated that the huge tumors of the lymphatic system were caused

by a kind of worm, called Filaria bancrofti, but almost everything about the life history of these worms was obscure. The
adult worms, two or three inches long, lived coiled up in the
lymphatic system, and these worms had been found to produce
millions of microscopic young, which could be detected in the
circulating blood. Since the development of the disease was very
slow, Manson reasoned that the microscopic worms in the blood
could not develop directly into the adult worms, else the human
host would very rapidly be taken over by the seething mass of
millions of worms. In constantly examining his patients, he made
the curious discovery that the microscopic forms were only
found in the blood at night. He reasoned that this might be an
adaptation to being picked up by some bloodsucking insect.

Manson, like many original discoverers, worked on a series of
wrong assumptions toward a right answer (the periodicity of the
worms is not now considered an adaptation to the vector). He
rejected fleas, bugs and lice as vectors of his filaria on the
grounds that if these were involved, elephantiasis would occur
everywhere in the world, and he picked mosquitoes for study on
the assumption that these were primarily tropical (there are 29
different kinds of mosquitoes in England). He let various Amoy
mosquitoes bite his patients, and discovered that in one kind,
called Culex fatigans, the worms picked up from the blood continued to develop. This was in 1877–78.

Manson did not complete the story, because he assumed that
a mosquito would bite only once. It seems curious to us now that
he or his contemporaries did not attempt to find out how many
times a mosquito might bite—it shows the limitations of human
thinking, which are always apparent to us when we examine history, but which must be hampering our own thinking, now, just
as much as in times past. Anyway, Manson presumed that the
mosquitoes must die when they laid their eggs on water, and that
the decaying mosquito would liberate the worms into the water,
whence they would get back into some new human host in drink-

ing water. It wasn't until sixteen years later that a man in Australia demonstrated that the worms get back into man by crawling down the proboscis of the mosquito on some subsequent bite, perhaps crawling into the hole in the skin made by the mosquito. It apparently takes such a worm about a year to reach maturity in the new host, but the details of this part of the life cycle are still not well known.

Manson went back to England in 1890 and settled down in London, where he became active in furthering the study of tropical medicine. He was largely responsible for the establishment of the famous London School of Tropical Medicine; but perhaps his greatest claim to fame lies in the suggestions and encouragement that he gave to Ronald Ross in developing the explanation of the transmission of malaria.

Ross worked in India, under all of the handicaps of unsympathetic army administration. He started out studying human malaria, and very soon found that the blood parasites of that disease would develop in Anopheles mosquitoes. But he was transferred to Calcutta, where malaria was scarce, and he was unable to complete his experiments to demonstrate transmission. But blood parasites very similar to those causing human malaria had been discovered in birds, so Ross, in Calcutta, turned his attention to these. In July, 1898, he finally demonstrated the complete developmental cycle of these malaria-like parasites in mosquitoes, clearly showing that mosquitoes were the vectors of the parasites from bird to bird. Within a few months of his announcement, an Italian, Amico Bignami, succeeded in causing an experimental human infection with malaria through the bite of an Anopheles mosquito, and soon after this Bignami, with Bastianelli and Grassi, demonstrated the complete transmission cycle of the human parasite.

I might note that the malaria parasites of man and of birds are quite different, in that the human species cannot infect birds, or vice versa. The parasites are all similar, belonging to a particular genus (Plasmodium) of protozoa, and they all are transmitted from vertebrate to vertebrate by mosquitoes. Four different kinds of malaria parasites are known from man, about fifteen from different kinds of birds, and eight or so from monkeys.

This work with malaria by Ross and by the Italians led directly to the famous studies of yellow fever carried out in 1900 in Cuba by the American Army Commission under the leadership of Walter Reed. Their dramatic experiments clearly proved that yellow fever was transmitted from man to man by a mosquito, Aedes aegypti. Progress in knowledge of the various insect-borne diseases was rapid after this, and today there is no technical reason why they should form a major threat to health in the tropics or anywhere else.

Malaria and yellow fever are very different diseases. About the only things they have in common are the fact that they are both transmitted by mosquitoes and the fact that they have both been major factors in the history of man in the tropics. Let's look at yellow fever first, since it is the more dramatic disease and the one that has been brought more completely under control.

Yellow fever is caused by a virus. Viruses have become the subject of very intensive study in recent years, but it is still difficult to say what they are. They are pathogens, causative agents of disease, that are too small to be seen with an ordinary microscope, small enough so that they pass through porcelain filters of known pore size that catch ordinary bacteria; and they are obligate parasites, incapable of life by themselves, so that they cannot be grown in the laboratory on ordinary bacterial culture media. Viruses may represent some primitive, as yet undeveloped form of life, though it seems to me more likely that they represent the final stage of degeneration through adaptation to parasitism. Parasites frequently go through a process of degeneration, of simplification of organization, as they come to depend more and more on their hosts; and viruses may represent the logical end stage of this process, in which nothing is left of the parasite except the basic attribute of reproduction: a final nuclear material that depends on host cells for all of the essentials of metabolism. Hence both the small size and obligate parasitism.

Whatever its real nature, the virus of yellow fever causes an acute, self-limited infection in man. If introduced into the blood stream, it multiplies with great rapidity, reaching a high concentration in body tissues within a few days. The curious antigenic system of the body starts to operate, as it does after the introduction of any strange protein, producing specific antibodies that are able to neutralize the effect of the virus. The course of the disease in the individual seems to depend on the result of this race between virus multiplication and antibody development. An attack of yellow fever may be so mild that symptoms are hardly discernible, or it may rapidly reach an acute stage, often characterized by stomach haemorrhage ("black vomit") and with extensive damage to liver tissues, which seems usually to be the immediate cause of death. Typically the human (or monkey) infection has run its course within two weeks, and the host is either dead or forever solidly immune against further attack by that particular kind of virus.

Reed and the other early workers on yellow fever were handicapped by the fact that man was the only known host: there were no laboratory animals with which the details of the disease could be studied; and the mortality rate in man was so high that tests had to be limited to a few courageous volunteers. With the discovery of the mosquito vector, however, the problem of control seemed to be solved. Yellow fever was cleaned out of Havana, and a few years later Gorgas gave a dramatic demonstration of the effectiveness of anti-mosquito measures in Panama, where yellow fever had defeated the earlier French efforts to dig a canal.

Yellow fever soon disappeared from the entire Caribbean

area, and it looked as though it ought to be possible to eliminate the disease entirely from the Western hemisphere, if not from the world. The Rockefeller Foundation started a campaign of investigation and control of yellow fever, about 1916, with this avowed objective. One of the early steps of the Foundation was to set up research laboratories in Nigeria and Brazil. The workers in Nigeria found almost at once that the disease could be given to the Indian rhesus monkey, which made it possible to study yellow fever in the laboratory. Supplies of these monkeys were shipped to Brazil, and between the two laboratories a great deal was learned about the disease in a very short time. It was a costly business, because a high proportion of the researchers became infected with the disease, and several of them died. But it was also one of the most dramatically successful of medical investigations, since it led, in a very few years, to the discovery of an immunizing vaccine, so that no one within reach of vaccination need ever be infected by yellow fever again.

But in Brazil and Colombia they also discovered that it would not be possible to eliminate yellow fever from the American continents. In the Caribbean the earlier epidemiological picture was correct: yellow fever was a disease of man, caused by a virus transmitted by the domestic mosquito Aedes aegypti, and thus susceptible of attack at several points in the cycle. In South America, however, the urban epidemics represented a spill-over from a reservoir of virus in the vast continental forests, maintained among the monkeys through transmission cycles involving purely forest mosquitoes. The spectacular urban epidemics here, as elsewhere, were caused by Aedes aegypti, and could be eliminated by the control of this mosquito. But the country people, in contact with the forest, could only be protected through vaccination. Control of the disease became a problem of organization—organization for the control of Aedes in the cities and towns, and for reaching the scattered farmers and woodcutters with vaccine.

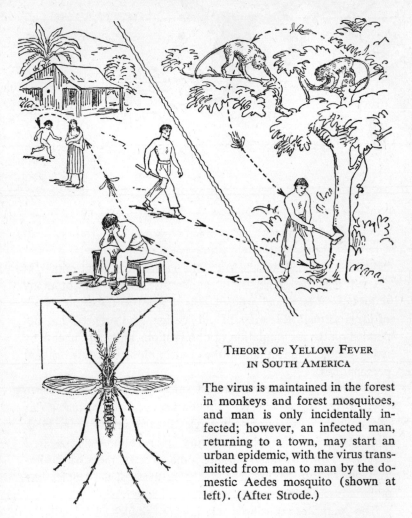

THEORY OF YELLOW FEVER
IN SOUTH AMERICA

The virus is maintained in the forest
in monkeys and forest mosquitoes,
and man is only incidentally infected; however, an infected man,
returning to a town, may start an
urban epidemic, with the virus transmitted from man to man by the domestic Aedes mosquito (shown at
left). (After Strode.)

The history of malaria is not as easy to summarize as that of
yellow fever. Studies of yellow fever have been limited to a few
laboratories, first because of its danger and then because of the
expense in apparatus, animals and training required for work
with a virus. Studies of malaria, on the other hand, have been

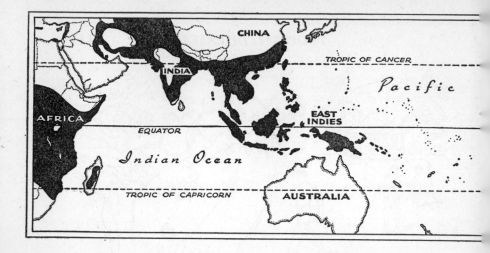

carried out by thousands of people, working in laboratories scattered all over the world. The study has become a special science, called malariology, which forms the exclusive subject matter of several scientific journals, of numerous books, and of many thousands of technical articles. It is difficult to trace the history of ideas through this mass of publication, and progress has depended on the accumulation of observations and experiments by many people, rather than on the contributions of a few brilliant personalities.

This immense concentration of study on malaria has been a result of the recognition by 20th century medicine of malaria as probably the most important single disease afflicting mankind. During the first half of the century it has almost disappeared from the United States and become greatly reduced in importance in Europe, but it is still, over most of the tropics, the major cause of sickness and death.

The parasites causing malaria are single-celled animals, Protozoa, belonging to the genus Plasmodium. Four species that can be recognized by their different appearance under the microscope are known from man; these differ somewhat in the symptoms they produce, and in virulence, so that human malaria really is not a single disease, but a collective term for several

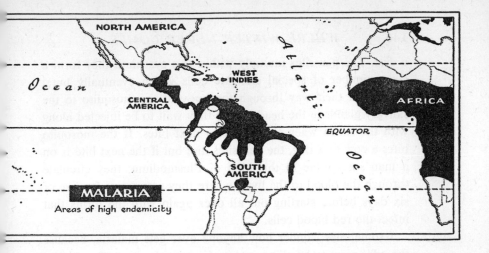

NORTH AMERICA

Atlantic

WEST INDIES

Ocean

CENTRAL AMERICA

AFRICA

EQUATOR

SOUTH AMERICA

Ocean

MALARIA

Areas of high endemicity

related diseases. The human parasites will not infect any other kind of an animal; but experimental work is possible with volunteers because laboratory infections, with modern drugs, can be easily controlled. A great deal of experimental work has been done with the distinct, but very similar, parasites of birds and monkeys.

The malaria parasite has a complicated life cycle. In man, the parasites live within the red blood cells. They reproduce by splitting and when a certain number of young parasites (usually sixteen) has accumulated in a cell, it bursts and each parasite seeks a new cell. Most of the millions of infected cells in a given person are apt to burst at about the same time, causing the characteristic periodicity in fever and chills.

At certain times (no one is quite sure why) a different sort of a parasite appears in some of the blood cells; these are the sexual forms, called gametocytes, that infect mosquitoes. If they remain in the blood, they eventually die; but if they are picked up by the right sort of mosquito, they are able to continue development. In the mosquito stomach they break free from the red blood cells, some as whip-like male cells, others as female cells; the two sorts fuse in the mosquito stomach to form something called a gamete. This gamete works into the stomach wall, where it forms a cyst. The parasites multiply within this cyst until they form a large number of special elongate cells which eventually burst free, work their way through the body of the mosquito to the salivary glands in the head, where they wait to be injected along with the saliva when the mosquito next bites. If the mosquito bites a cow or a dog, the parasites die; but if the next bite is on a man susceptible to this kind of Plasmodium, they circulate through the blood to the liver, where they recuperate for five or six days before starting out all over again with the forms that infect the red blood cells.

I sometimes wonder how anyone ever gets malaria, because the odds seem to be all against it. A particular kind of mosquito (an Anopheles) must bite a man at a time when gametocytes are circulating in his blood. This mosquito must survive the hazards of nature for at least ten days while the parasite completes the cycle in his body; and the hazards of nature for a mosquito are considerable, so that the great majority surely die before the ten days have passed. Then the mosquito, when it bites again, must bite a susceptible man—not a horse or a sparrow or a man who already has that kind of malaria. It takes infinite pains to keep mosquitoes and malaria going in the laboratory; and out in nature, with no one to look after them, I don't see how the mosquitoes and the parasites get along at all. Yet millions of people get infected every year, and the whole method of getting from man to man must be considered a great success from the parasite's point of view.

Of course, this very complexity helps in designing control measures. There are more than two hundred different kinds of Anopheles mosquitoes in the world, and all of them could transmit malaria, but only a few do. Many are too rare to be important; others never live long enough; some rarely bite man, preferring other animals. The important malaria vectors are a few species that live in close association with man. These can be avoided by house screening, or their breeding places destroyed by drainage or treatment with insecticides. The most dramatic results of all have been obtained by spraying the houses with D.D.T. This does not kill all of the mosquitoes in the neighborhood, but it kills those individuals that have bitten or would bite men, thus cutting out malaria transmission. By systematic and thorough treatment of this sort, malaria can sometimes be completely eliminated from an area in a few years. Also the old stand-by of quinine has now been replaced by more efficient drugs, so that where medical attention is available, infected people can be cured, leaving nothing for the mosquitoes to transmit. This is the least hopeful method of control, because in most malarious areas, medical attention simply is not available for most of the population. It is far more economical to attack the disease through the mosquitoes than through the human host.

With filariasis (elephantiasis), yellow fever and malaria, we have not exhausted the list of diseases transmitted by mosquitoes. But these are the most important, and they show how mosquitoes can act as vectors for three very different kinds of parasites—microscopic worms, viruses, and protozoa.

Mosquitoes are not the only insect vectors of disease. Typhus fever is transmitted to man by lice and fleas; but typhus is hardly a tropical disease, since it may occur anywhere under conditions of overcrowding and dirt. Relapsing fever, caused by a spirochaete and transmitted by lice and ticks, is also widespread.

The most famous of the tropical insect-borne diseases, after yellow fever and malaria, is African sleeping-sickness. This is caused by a parasitic protozoan, Trypanosoma, and transmitted by a biting fly, Glossina. There is a similar disease of cattle in tropical Africa, called nagana, also caused by a trypanosome and also transmitted by Glossina. The relation between the cattle disease and the human disease is still not certain, despite careful and extensive investigations, but both diseases are very important in tropical African economy.

Some of the earliest accounts of sleeping sickness concerned slaves brought to the West Indies. The final, lethargic stage of the disease only sets in when the central nervous system becomes involved, which may not occur until a year or more after infection, so that apparently healthy slaves would not develop the symptoms until after arrival in the New World. It was generally assumed that these slaves were dying of "homesickness." The disease never became established in America because the necessary vector, the tsetse fly, was not present.

The disease was most often noticed in slaves in the 19th century because Europeans did not penetrate to the infested areas away from the coast, whence the slaves were brought. For a time, it was thought that Europeans were not susceptible. This soon enough proved to be wrong, though the disease seems never to have been very common among Europeans, probably because they stay away from infested areas.

Sleeping sickness was probably originally rather local and limited in its distribution, spreading much more widely with the "opening up" of the continent by Europeans, with consequent movements of people and cattle. It is thought, for instance, that Henry Stanley first brought the disease to the Lake region of East Africa in 1887 when he went up the Congo on the Emin Pasha Relief Expedition with a company of over 700 men.

The tsetse flies stay close to "bush" and bite only during the daytime. Travelers consequently try to pass at night through areas known to be dangerous. Much of central Africa is covered with a grassland, with forest growing only in narrow belts along the streams: stream fords, in such regions, would be the dangerous places for tsetse, and one method of control has been through making broad clearings at such fords. With clearing, the fly and the disease retreat, which has long been a potent argument for deforestation in Africa. Since many kinds of game carry trypanosomes, some of which are probably capable of causing the cattle and perhaps the human diseases, extermination of game has also been proposed. Tsetse fly control thus poses many problems where the interests of the public health men and the conservation workers seem to be in conflict.

The tsetse fly itself is curious because of its method of reproduction. It is a brownish fly, rather larger than a house fly; and

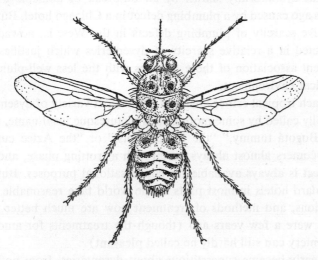

The Tsetse Fly, Glossina, Vector of African Sleeping-Sickness.

it must be especially tough and free from enemies because the adults, if they can get a regular supply of blood, live for many months—an unusual longevity for an insect. The female does not lay eggs, like "normal" insects. Instead, a single larva is nourished within the body of the mother until it is full grown, when it is dropped on the soil in a shaded place. The larva crawls into the soil, pupates, and emerges as an adult a few weeks later. A female produces such a larva about every two weeks. To the best of my knowledge, this is the lowest reproduction rate known for any insect. Most other kinds of flies lay hundreds or thousands of eggs, depending on the chance survival of a few of them for the continuation of the species.

I suppose that any account of tropical diseases should include some mention of dysenteries, and of the more bizarre kinds of tropical worms. Dysenteries, of course, are no more peculiarly tropical than most of the rest of the so-called tropical diseases— as was dramatically shown by an outbreak of amoebic a few years ago caused by a plumbing defect in a Chicago hotel. But the relative scarcity of plumbing defects in the West is, nowadays, reflected in a relative scarcity of dysenteries which justifies the present association of these diseases with the less well-plumbed tropical environment.

Each tropical center boasts of its own pet variety of dysentery, usually called by some more or less picturesque local name, such as "Bogotá tummy," "the tourist trots," or "the Aztec curse." Newcomers almost always go through a trotting phase, and the subject is always available for conversational purposes. But the standard hotels in most parts of the world take reasonable precautions, and methods of treatment now are much better than they were a few years ago (though the treatments for amoebic dysentery can still hardly be called pleasant).

I early became superstitious about dysenteries, from noticing that the people who were most scared of them were apt to get the most severe attacks. Such people would take extreme precautions, boiling their own water or living on tea and imported, bottled water, avoiding uncooked foods, and staying away from all of the interesting places—and yet come down with the most virulent forms of dysentery. Partly the problem is to distinguish between biological cleanliness and apparent cleanliness: the clear water of a village well may be very dangerous, while the muddy water of an Amazon tributary may be perfectly safe.

It is surprising how often one encounters people who will not eat salads, or drink unboiled water, and yet have not taken the trouble to have a careful medical examination made of their servants. Eating only cooked food is no protection, either, if the food has been left around in a place where a few flies could crawl over it. The proper course, in any particular place, is to make some calculation of the sort of precautions that might most reasonably be taken to avoid infections; and then, these precautions having been adopted, to cease to worry until the pressure of events seems to make medical consultation advisable.

Of tropical worms, the one that has always fascinated me most is the guinea-worm, although I have never seen one. It occurs only in certain parts of tropical Africa and India. My fascination stems from the pictures of the local method of extracting the worm by slowly winding it, an inch or so a day for a couple of weeks on a small stick, as it emerges from the leg muscles in which it has developed. The guinea-worm, like most of these tropical worms, has a complicated life history, and human infection comes from drinking water containing copepods (minute, shrimp-like crustacea) which are infected with an intermediate stage of the worm. The adult worm in a man's leg may liberate large numbers of microscopic larvae into water when the human host goes wading, and these larvae head for the copepods, and hence with the water down the gullet of some subsequent drinker. Europeans, taking even the most rudimentary precautions, are unlikely to be drinking water from an infected source, so the worm is no hazard to the traveler. And local control, as in the case of so many diseases, depends on proper sanitary precautions with the village water supply.

I have had a great deal of experience with one tropical worm, the human bot-fly, or Dermatobia. This is the larva of a fly that develops in a boil-like sore on the skin of man or of various other animals (especially cattle). For the most part it is rare, and unlikely to be encountered by visitors; but it happened, for some reason unknown to us, to be extremely common in the region where we lived in Colombia.

The adult fly, like so many of these tropical parasites, goes about its business in a very indirect manner. Instead of laying its eggs directly on a man, it comes and sits on the man's shoulders in a tame and friendly fashion, waiting for a mosquito to come along and bite. When a mosquito or other small fly arrives, the Dermatobia pounces on it, and hovering, clasps it tightly for a few minutes while it lays a cluster of eggs on the mosquito's abdomen. These eggs take about a week to develop. At the end of that time, they break open, and the tiny Dermatobia larva hangs within the eggshell until the mosquito comes again to a man or some other warm-blooded animal to bite. Then, under the stimulus of this proximity to warm skin, the larva drops off and burrows into the nearest sweat pore, where it starts to eat and grow.

The victim first notices a small bump, like that resulting from some insect bite. But the bump persists and gets larger, and after a week or so there will be an occasional sharp pain at the infected spot. The little larva that is growing there is big at one end and tapering at the other; and the big end is armed with a series of sharp, black spines, that make the whole thing look like an Indian war club. I suspect that these sharp pains result when the worm turns over, grating some nerve-ends with these spines. If the spot is examined with a hand lens, it will be found to center in a tiny hole, where the worm periodically comes up for air.

We were making mosquito collections in forests where these flies were common, and some of the men had thirty or more such worms in their skin at a time. I think my own record was six or seven at once, which was bad enough, though the men took it as all part of the day's work. We got quite expert at getting the worms out, which is something of a trick because they hang on inside with those spines. If the worm is broken and part of it left inside, infection is likely to result. We had many methods of extraction, but the neatest was to hold a lighted cigarette close to the skin, making the worm uncomfortably warm so that he relaxed his hold and, with an appropriately timed squeeze, could be popped out. This required considerable skill, and a more routine method was to cover the wormhole tightly with adhesive tape. The worm would then be smothered in about 24 hours and, dead, could easily be squeezed out.

Any account of tropical diseases, like the one I have attempted here, makes the region sound like a pretty horrid place. I cannot deny that the diseases are present, and I think that they constitute the primary barrier to the achievement of a more pleasant and satisfactory life for millions of tropical peoples. The conditions themselves are in part a result of the modern explosion of Western civilization which resulted in the transfer and spread of parasites all through the tropics, and in many changes in ways of life that made locally adapted peoples more exposed to the hazards of disease.

But Western civilization has also made extraordinary progress in the understanding and control of these diseases; and with the methods presently available, there is no technical reason why the tropics should not be just as healthy as any other part of the earth's surface. I remarked in a previous chapter that I thought the development of civilized culture in Western Europe was contingent on the discovery of a few ways of modifying the climatic environment through the development of methods of heating, lighting and housing. It seems to me that in an entirely comparable manner, further progress toward the realization of ever more satisfactory levels of culture (for the peoples concerned) in the tropical region may be dependent on the development of the control of disease.

With modern insecticides, drugs and methods of application, we have the technical means of accomplishing this. But if these means are to be effective, they must be adopted and understood by the local peoples who are most concerned. The urgent present problems, then, are not so much medical, as sociological or anthropological: how to fit the technologies that have been developed by Western science into the cultures that have been developed by man in the tropics; or how to assist in the modification of those cultures so that the technologies can be accepted.

★

CHAPTER X

Food and Drink

EOPLE have been eating for a long time now—eating
their way through the course of evolution from primate
to human status; eating as primitive savages and eating as
civilized savages; eating in the arctic, in the tropical forests, on
the sea islands; eating all kinds of things, from dirt to other
people. Food, then, as a common denominator of all men, should
stand part from the influences of history, geography and culture;
should provide a basis for formulations leading to mutual understanding among men.

It turns out, however, that food is nothing of the sort. All men
do have in common a particular kind of a digestive and eating
apparatus, and a similar drive of hunger; but the materials that
they stuff into this apparatus, that they search for in response
to this hunger drive, are as diverse as any other aspect of their
cultures. Food, instead of being a basis for common understanding, becomes a basis for scorn, arrogance, ridicule and misunderstanding: as culture-bound as clothes, language or religion.

I suspect that even the science of nutrition is culture-bound.
It arose, after all, as a part of Western civilization, and it has
been preoccupied with Western food materials and food habits.
It works pretty well within this Western context, where the rapid
"advance" in methods of food processing and refining had to be

counterbalanced by a scientific advance that could replace lost nutritive values with pills, impregnations, irradiations and what not. But nutrition experts, when removed from their cultural context, often seem at a loss. Some of them appear to be horrified at the fact that non-Western peoples eat non-Western foods, and there is a tendency to try to remedy this situation by attempting to persuade the Chinese to drink their milk or the Arabs to eat their spinach.

Many of the tropical peoples, clearly, are ill-nourished or under-nourished by any standards; but others appear to be remarkably healthy even though living on diets that seem to us bizarre. To determine what these peoples actually eat, what is the food value of these materials, and how to make changes or substitutions when these seem desirable, will not be easy. But the start that has been made with such studies indicates that there is a fascinating field for work here, likely to produce information of great use to ourselves as well as to the tropical peoples directly concerned.

But I intended to write in this chapter about tropical foods and drinks, not about tropical nutrition—in other words, about what people eat rather than about what they ought to eat. That is a hard enough job because they eat so many different things. About all I can do is give some account of the cereals and starches that serve as staples of diet, mention a few of the varied tropical fruits that always attract the attention of the Westerner who goes south, and say something about the origin of various tropical drinks like tea, coffee and chocolate that now form a principal export of the tropics to the West.

If any generalization can be made about tropical diets, it is that they are predominantly vegetarian. This is because domestic animals are not common enough to be a major source of food supply, except in the grassland fringes of the tropics. As with any generalization, all sorts of exceptions come to mind. The Latin Americans, for instance, have tended to retain food-habits brought from Spain or Portugal, including a high meat consumption. And coastal peoples, of course, depend greatly on fish and other produce of the sea everywhere. Nowadays pigs and chickens have penetrated almost all parts of the tropics, to provide materials for celebrations and feasts, if not to serve as daily staples of the diet.

But the basic diet, still, is vegetarian; and the principal constituent, around much of the globe's circumference, is rice.

The origins of rice, like those of most of man's domesticated plants, are obscure. "Wild rice" is found in many parts of the world, including America and Australia, but the cultivated form probably arose from a wild type found in India. I have not been very successful in trying to track down information on the role of rice in the early civilizations of the Orient, perhaps because I have not found the right books, or perhaps because Western scholars have been little interested in the matter. The early civilizations of Mesopotamia, Egypt and the Mediterranean were based on wheat, and this has been discussed by many authors from botanical, archeological and historical points of view. I think there must have been ancient cultures in tropical Asia based on rice, but I have no documentation for this.

The Far Eastern or Chinese civilization was based on wheat in the north and rice in the south, and the study of the cultural relations between the two cereals may thus be a task of Chinese scholarship. It is only in the Far East, in China and Japan, that rice has become a basic cereal in a non-tropical civilization.

The rice-eating peoples have suffered greatly from their contact with our own Western culture, because this contact has introduced machine methods of processing rice that strip it of all accessory food elements, leaving only the plain starch of polished rice. Traditional methods of preparation in India and elsewhere resulted in a much more wholesome food; but these methods have not held up in competition with the modern mills, and anyway the foolish people prefer the bright, clean, polished rice, even though it does give them beriberi. So the problem now, as with machine-milled wheat, is to find methods of putting the vitamins back in rice without spoiling its pretty appearance.

When we lived in Colombia, we arranged to get rice from a local mill before it had gone through the final polishing process. I must confess that it had a slightly odd taste that we never quite got used to, but we carried on in the conviction that it was "good for us." The rice polishings, so rich in vitamins, were sold as animal food. We tried getting this and cooking it in various ways, but no matter how it was prepared, it tasted awful. So, although I deplore the Westernizing process that has taken the nutritive value out of rice, I sympathize with the people who persist in eating the unwholesome but beautiful polished product.

The answer, perhaps, lies in the sauce. The Eastern peoples have long made up their curries and other rice dishes with all sorts of tasty oddments that must, surely, be rich in vitamins and all of the rest of the catalogue of nutritive elements. And rice, I think, should always have its sauce. Plain, it is a very dull food, no better than the oatmeal of the Scots. But as a base on which to build with piquant sauces, I think it is the best staple food man has yet developed.

The next most important tropical cereal, after rice, is maize or Indian corn. This is an extraordinary plant, differing from all of the other grasses in having its seeds neatly arranged on a sheathed cob. Such an arrangement is very convenient for man, making the grain easy to harvest and store, but it has no imaginable utility from the point of view of the plant. Maize, in fact, is completely domesticated, completely dependent on man for gathering and planting its seeds. It never "goes wild," and no wild plant with this sheathed pod arrangement is known.

The origin of this very useful cereal has long puzzled botanists and archeologists. It is surely an American plant. It formed the basic food supply for the great civilizations of Central and South America, and was widely cultivated by the Indians of both of the

American continents, but unknown outside of the Western hemisphere until its discovery by the first expedition of Columbus in 1492. In America it has been cultivated for a long time, however, and maize remains have been found associated with archeological material dating back at least to 2000 B.C.

The post-Columbian history of maize through the world would make an interesting study from the point of view of cultural differences. Some peoples accepted it readily. It penetrated parts of Africa well ahead of the European explorers, and in parts of the Balkans and Italy it early became a staple cereal. France and England, however, found no use for it; and in England today, I believe it is chiefly cultivated as a garden ornamental. Over much of tropical America it remains the basic food; and it is probably the most important single plant in the economy of the United States, achieving this position more through its use as animal food, than as a direct part of the human diet.

The peoples of the highlands of Mexico and Guatemala still cling to their ancestral dependence on maize as the basic human food, and they have developed what seem to me to be the most satisfactory ways of preparing it: the freshly ground meal rolled out flat and baked in pancake form on hot stones to make *tortillas*; or boiled in corn husk or banana leaf wrappings, with all sorts of tasty inclusions, to make the different varieties of *tamales*.

We tend to think of maize as a very incomplete human food, because the malnutrition among the corn-pone eaters of our own south has become so notorious. But nutrition studies carried out in Mexico indicate that *tortillas,* prepared in the Indian fashion, have a much greater food value than bread prepared from the corn meal of our commerce. Also, of course, the Mexicans use a wider variety of supplementary foods than do the poor whites of our south: especially beans for protein and red peppers for vitamins. The Mexican also gets many vitamins very pleasantly from his fermented drink, *pulque.* Maize meal itself is allowed to ferment by many peoples, thus acquiring vitamins from the yeasts.

I find an editorial comment on this in the staid *British Medical Journal.* "Missionaries have sometimes quite properly tried to suppress the evils of drink among their native converts, only to find them falling mysteriously ill: the ban on native beer removes the native's only source of vitamin-B complex. Platt and Webb, in a study of Kaffir beer, which is brewed from maize, point out that, while maize-eaters are notoriously liable to pellagra, this nicotinic-acid-deficiency disease is never seen among maize-beer drinkers because during the fermenting yeast synthesizes nicotinic acid and riboflavin, so that the drink contains more than the grain from which it is made."

The northern cereals, like wheat, barley and oats, are cultivated in the highlands in many parts of the tropics; but they are usually associated with intrusions of European culture, and need concern us little here. In the lowland tropics, rice and maize are the two most common and most widely distributed foods, but they are far from universal as the basis of diet, and it may be interesting to examine some of the other starch sources, like cassava, breadfruit, and sweet potatoes.

Cassava or mandioc (the botanical name is Manihot) was the staple food plant of most of the Indians of the lowland tropics in pre-Columbian America. It is still the staple food of the Brazilian Indians. It is an important food in many other parts of Latin America, and its cultivation has spread to parts of the Asiatic and African tropics. It is the source of the tapioca of commerce.

The cassava plants are scraggly shrubs belonging to the plant family Euphorbiaceae, which includes spurge, poinsettias, the castor-oil bean, and many other plants with milky, often poisonous sap. Cassava has large, fleshy roots, which may be two or three feet long and six inches or more in diameter, with a very high starch content. There are two cultivated species. The kind commonly used by the Indians of interior South America is called bitter cassava, and its roots contain hydrocyanic acid so that they are poisonous before preparation. How man discovered that this poisonous root could be an important food source has

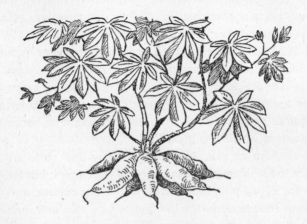

Cassava (Manihot utilissima).

always puzzled me. Yet, as I pointed out in Chapter IV, agriculture may have originated with these root crops, which makes it possible that cassava was the first plant to be cultivated in America.

There are many ways of preparing cassava, as is true of all of these staple foods. The different tribes have various ways of pressing out the poisonous juice, which may then be cooked down to make a sauce, since the poison is destroyed by heat. The starchy pulp of the root may be baked in the form of cakes, or it may be dried and prepared as a flour which can be easily transported or stored.

Cassava, like maize, is frequently used as the basis for a fermented drink. Here we come across the very widespread practice, used by many different primitive peoples in various parts of the world, of making the drink by chewing the starchy material and spitting it into a common trough. The ptyalin in the saliva changes part of the starch into sugar and so hastens fermentation by giving the yeast a quicker start. Here again one

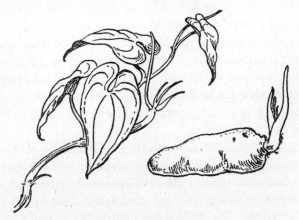

Yam (Dioscorea).

wonders how the discovery came to be made, apparently quite independently in different parts of the world.

Sweet potatoes and yams should also be mentioned among the tropical sources of starchy food. The sweet potato, like cassava, is an American plant which was cultivated in both the Andean and the Mayan centers of civilization, as well as by many less advanced peoples. But it seems also to have spread in pre-Columbian times over much of Polynesia and Melanesia.

The yam, on the contrary, is an Old World plant, perhaps first cultivated in Java or southern India, but spreading all through tropical Asia at a very early date. Yet there is some evidence, such as a description of the plant by Oviedo, indicating that it was cultivated in the West Indies at the time of their discovery by the Spaniards.

These root crops, at best, are not as easily stored or transported as the cereals, so they seem never to have formed the basic food of any very complex civilization. This civilized cultural level apparently depends on a fairly dense concentration of people and on a considerable specialization of labor, which means that the agriculturists must support the accumulation of artisans, priests, warriors, scholars, artists and so forth. And in the tropics maize and rice have been the only foods capable of supporting such a nonagricultural superstructure. Perhaps the failure of peoples in tropical Africa to produce an indigenous civilization was due to failure to discover or adopt some such efficient crop at an early period, rather than to factors of race, climate or physiography.

These root crops have, however, served as important supplementary sources of starch for the civilizations; and they have been sufficient to support the development of some very attractive cultures, even though these have fallen short of the criteria of "civilization." The Polynesian culture, for instance, had no cereal, though its agriculture was well developed. The Polynesians are said to have introduced something like a hundred different plants into the Hawaiian Islands, many of them kinds propagated by cuttings, and all of them carried over long sea voyages in open boats. Their staples, their prime sources of starch, were yams, taro and breadfruit.

The breadfruit grows on a large, handsome tree belonging to the plant family Moraceae, which also includes the mulberry and the fig. It is probably native to the East Indies, though it has been anciently cultivated all through tropical Asia and the Pacific. The fruit itself is round or oval, four to eight inches in diameter, with a slightly roughened surface which becomes brownish or yellow when the fruit is mature. The starchy pulp is white in the immature fruit, yellowish when fully ripe. The varieties that are most commonly cultivated contain no seeds, but are propagated by means of sprouts from the roots. The

Polynesians thus had to carry the young trees with them in their voyages to new islands, in order to spread its cultivation.

The voyage of Captain Bligh on H.M.S. *Bounty,* which has become famous because of the mutiny, was made for the purpose

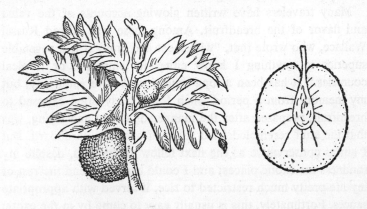

Breadfruit (Artocarpus incisa).

of carrying the breadfruit tree from the South Seas to the West Indies. A thousand young trees were loaded on the ship in Tahiti; but the crew, in the course of these loading operations, had become enchanted with the Tahitian way of life, and before the ship had got very far, mutinied, and eventually established themselves on Pitcairn's Island, where their descendants now offer a rich material for anthropological and social study. Captain Bligh made another attempt in 1792, and that time collected 1,200 breadfruit plants, as well as other valuable trees, which he brought safely to the West Indies.

Of its preparation, W. E. Safford writes: "It is eaten before it becomes ripe, while the pulp is still white and mealy, of a consistency intermediate between new bread and sweet potatoes. In Guam it was formerly cooked after the manner of most Pacific island aborigines, by means of heated stones in a hole in the earth, layers of stones, breadfruit and green leaves alternating. It is still sometimes cooked this way on ranches; but the usual way of cooking it is to boil it or to bake it in ovens; or it is cut in slices and fried like potatoes. This last method is the one usually preferred by foreigners."

Many travelers have written glowing accounts of the value and flavor of the breadfruit. Among these was Alfred Russel Wallace, who wrote that, "with meat and gravy it is a vegetable superior to anything I know either in temperate or tropical countries." It has been a long time since I have eaten any; but my memory from a period when I was fairly often exposed to breadfruit, prepared after the manner of slicing and frying, was that the stuff resembled fried slices of a friable cardboard. But I am as conservative as the next fellow about food, despite my fondness for exotic places; and I could happily spend the rest of my life pretty much restricted to rice, if served with appropriate sauces. Fortunately, this is usually easy to come by in the exotic places.

I vote that we skip the vegetables, in this survey of tropical foods, and go on to the fruits. This is a pretty large order in itself. I have just gone over the table of contents of Wilson Popenoe's book on tropical fruits, and I find that he discusses some 81 different kinds in some detail, though he does not include the citrus fruits, nor the banana, coconut or pineapple. Obviously any coverage of this material in a few pages will have to be highly selective.

I think that in general fruits are a much more important part of the tropical diet than of the temperate zone diet. This is not obvious, because you do not often see in the tropics systematic cultivation of fruit trees on a large scale, like the vast commercial orchards of the temperate zone. Yet, despite this commercialization, fruits in the north seem to be almost a luxury food. Over most of the tropics, fruit cultivation is a dooryard affair, with the fruits constantly available to the rural population.

Something or other is ripe at all times of year, and I suspect that the constant nibbling of these varied fruits provides the people with an important source of supplementary food materials, such as vitamins. Even in the great cities, the markets are always heaped with a bewildering variety of edible fruits, and I have often marvelled that these great supplies could be gathered from the scattered dooryard plantings that seem to be the only possible source.

Fruit cultivation, fruit marketing, and fruit consumption are thus largely in the hands of the peasants and farmers, and hardly susceptible to study by the routine methods of the economists and statisticians. It is possible to get figures on the per capita consumption of rice in Java, for instance, and on its cost, which in turn can be translated into some formula for comparisons of "standards of living." But no one bothers about the per capita consumption of mangos, durians, bananas, and oranges in a place like Java, because they do not enter into the recognized Western-type channels of commerce. Yet I am sure that this fruit consumption would be important in any evaluation of the standards of living, or dietary balance, of the Javanese or any other tropical people.

Fruit cultivation is an older and better established part of the local folkways in some tropical regions than it is in the north. The Mediterranean cultures, with their tropical orientation, emphasized fruit culture—indeed, the vine and the olive were, after wheat, their most important crops. The Romans spread fruit growing northward with their conquests, as far as climatic conditions allowed. But the list of fruits known in the Mediterranean region was not large, as compared with any tropical region; and for many of our present European fruits and methods of cultivation, we are indebted to the medieval Moslem invaders, who brought both products and ideas from the East to Europe.

Of the citrus fruits, only the relatively inedible citron was known to the ancient Mediterranean. The sour orange, lemon and lime were brought to Europe by returning crusaders, who found them under cultivation by the Arabs. There is no mention of the sweet orange, however, in either European or Arabic literature before the fifteenth century. One theory has it that the orange was first brought in by Vasco da Gama on his return from the voyage to India in 1498, though it seems equally probable that it was brought back by Genoese traders at about the same time. It was certainly widely cultivated in tropical Asia and east Africa in the fifteenth century, and its cultivation spread rapidly in the Mediterranean in the following century.

The origin of all of the citrus fruits is obscure, although on botanical grounds it seems likely that they all came from tropical Asia, where there are many wild relatives with more or less edible fruits. They have surely been cultivated from remote antiquity, and the kinds that we know best, the oranges, lemons, limes and grapefruit, probably arose under cultivation, through hybridization and domestication. At least there are no known wild species corresponding to the different cultivated species.

Oranges and their kin are the best known of tropical fruits to northern peoples, because they can be cultivated in subtropical areas like the Mediterranean, Florida and California, and because they can be easily shipped for great distances. Probably within the tropics themselves, the citrus varieties are also first in importance among the fruits, though I am far from sure about this. Their closest rival and possible leader would be another fruit from the Asiatic tropics, the mango. This, like the citrus fruits, has spread around the globe in post-Columbian times; but it is less well known to northerners than citrus because it is more strictly tropical in climatic requirements, more difficult to ship and store, and because the finer varieties are hard to reproduce, so that in many regions only inferior sorts are known.

A few paragraphs above, I wrote that you do not often see large fruit orchards in the tropics. I find, however, that Popenoe's account of the mango starts with the statement that "Akbar, the

Mughal emperor who reigned in northern India from 1556 to 1605, planted near Darbhanga the Lakh Bagh, an orchard of a hundred thousand mango trees." As Popenoe goes on to say, "few other fruits have the historic background of the mango,

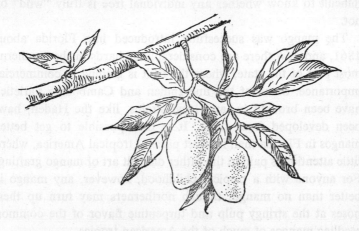

Mango (Mangifera indica).

and few others are so inextricably connected with the folklore and religious ceremonies of a great people. Buddha himself was presented with a mango grove, that he might find repose beneath its grateful shade."

The mango may well have been the first fruit tree to be cultivated by man; certainly it was among the first. Its antiquity is indicated by one of its Sanskrit names, *am*, which has an alternative meaning of provisions or victuals. It is important in Hindu mythology and ceremonial, and in the folklore of other Asiatic peoples. It was probably first brought to the New World by the Portuguese, about 1700. It spread throughout the American tropics in the 18th century, and now seems an integral part of the native flora. I remember once wandering in the Trinidad Mountains of Central Cuba in what I thought was a splendid, primitive forest until I came across some ancient mango trees. Whether they represented the remains of some old plantation, or whether they were "escapes," I do not know. The tree grows so readily in the forest both in India and in America that it is difficult to know whether any individual tree is truly "wild" or not.

The mango was succesfully introduced into Florida about 1861, and now there are considerable orchards in the southernmost part of the state, where the fruit is gaining in commercial importance. Some of the fine Indian and Cambodian varieties have been brought in, and local strains, like the Haden, have been developed from these. It is thus possible to get better mangos in Florida than in most parts of tropical America, where little attention is paid to the rather difficult art of mango grafting. For anyone with a tropical childhood, however, any mango is better than no mango; though northerners may turn up their noses at the stringy pulp and turpentine flavor of the common seedling mangos of much of the American tropics.

I suspect that any northerner would list the banana as far more important among tropical fruits than the mango. This would be true in terms of the commercial statistics so dear to the Western heart, since bananas form the basis of one of the greatest fruit industries, supporting fleets of steamships and furnishing the economic backbone of export for several different nations. But in terms of local diet, bananas are not of great importance anywhere in the tropics; they are not nearly as important, for instance, as their relatives, the plantains, which must be cooked, and which in many places furnish the staple source of starch.

Bananas, plantains and their relatives, like the other fruits that we have mentioned so far, originated in tropical Asia and have a long history of cultivation there. The cultivated bananas and plantains, in fact, do not produce viable seeds, so that, like so many domesticated plants, they have become completely dependent on man for propagation, which in itself would indicate a long human association.

Probably the majority of the fruits now widely cultivated

Plantain (Musa paradisiaca).

through the tropics had their origin in the rich peninsulas and islands of southeastern Asia; but the American tropics have made important contributions, too: the pineapple, the avocado, the guava, the papaya, and many less well-known fruits like the various sapotes and anonas.

The listing of these names brings back a host of associations. I was brought up in southern Florida by a horticultural father, who turned his place into a sort of botanical garden dedicated especially to tropical fruits. I have known David Fairchild, the

great plant explorer, since those boyhood days in Florida—he
has been my father-in-law for quite a few years now—and I have
tasted all sorts of outlandish things at his bidding, and spent
many hours listening to his accounts of the virtues, history and
usages of this fruit or that. On my first job out of college, my
chief was Wilson Popenoe, who has long been our leading
authority on horticulture in tropical America. All of this should
have made me a botanist or a horticulturist, and I still do not
know why it failed unless because it provoked a straight rebellion
against the pressures of the environment.

It had, however, at least one positive result: it gave associations and meanings to words like "anona" and "guava" that they
might never otherwise have acquired. "Guava" for me does not
mean a nasty mess of pulp, seeds and worms used for making
jelly. It means, instead, a horticultural possibility that has not
yet been realized. Hardly any two guavas are alike: they run a
wide gamut in size, color, flavor and texture, a mass of material
waiting for the hand of the skillful plant breeder. They grow
everywhere now in dooryards through the tropics, some with
very fine fruit that would please the most fastidious, others with
fruit that no one except the neighborhood children would touch.
Such studies as have been made indicate a high food value for
guavas—if I remember correctly they have a particularly high
content of vitamin C.

Surely one answer to the problems of nutrition in the tropics
lies in further work with fruits like this—in the development of
superior varieties, and in their establishment as articles of commerce and diet. I wrote earlier that I thought fruits were more
important in the tropical than in the temperate diet; but this does
not mean that fruit possibilities are anything like as fully realized
as they could or should be. This is particularly true in areas
where Western methods of industrialization and plantation agriculture have become established, resulting in a dense population
cut off from the traditional resource of dooryard foraging: for

such people fruits, like meat, may become a rare luxury. To restore the balance, it seems to me that attention should be given to possible local sources of the needed food elements; and that among such sources, tropical fruits would not be the least important.

But I entitled this chapter "food and drink," and yet so far I have not got beyond a sketchy account of cereals, other starches and fruit. Man does not live by food alone—he also drinks. And a great many of the things he drinks derive from the tropics.

In my original sketch for this chapter, I planned to give some account of the variety of tropical products that man has learned to ferment, and of his repeated discovery of the virtues of alcohol in different cultures and in different environments. The subject is fascinating enough, but on reflection, I think it would be a digression from the general theme of this book. After all, the Dionysian tradition is not a characteristically tropical tradition— rather it is characteristically human, independent of clime.

It is curious, though, that the great rebellion against the Dionysian tradition should occur in a tropical religion, Mohammedanism; and that the spread of this religion should be the chief agent in the establishment of a truly tropical beverage, coffee.

Mohammed did not know about coffee, else he might have prohibited it as well as wine and suchlike intoxicants. Presumably coffee has been grown and drunk in its home in the Abyssinian highlands since time immemorial, but its use seems not to have spread until the Arabs discovered the possibilities of the roasted seeds, some time after the establishment of the Mohammedan religion through the Near East. Coffee met considerable opposition from the orthodox Mohammedans, as did tobacco at a later date, because it was held to fall within the general prohibition against intoxicants. But the orthodox opposition was unavailing: coffee fitted too neatly into a scheme of life deprived of wine; and it was too useful in helping to keep the devout awake through the long ceremonials of their religion. After the fifteenth century, coffee became firmly established as the national drink of Arabia, and indeed of the whole Moslem world.

Coffee (Coffea arabica).

Tea probably originated in tropical India; it has a longer written history than coffee, since it was early adopted by the literate Chinese, but its pre-Chinese history, like the pre-Arabic history of coffee, is purely mythological. One Chinese legend attributes the introduction of tea to a Buddhist missionary named Bodhidharma. The missionary had vowed that he would contemplate the virtues of Buddha through nine unsleeping years. At the end of three years, he slept, and in his anger at this lapse, he cut off his eyelids and threw them on the ground beside him. After a further five years, he again felt drowsy; but this time, plucking some leaves from a shrub beside him, he found stimulation to complete the nine years of the vow. The leaves, of course, were of tea.

The tropical American contribution to this beverage list is

chocolate, or cacao. Cacao was very important in the ancient
civilizations of Central America. The cacao beans were used as
currency, and the Mayan god of cacao, Ek Chuah, was also the
god of merchants. It is said that a good slave could be purchased

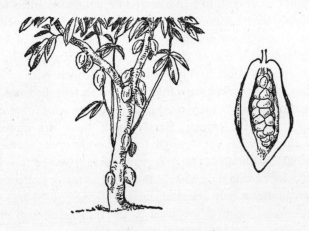

Cacao (Theobroma cacao).

with 100 cacao beans, which may attest either to the importance
of cacao or the cheapness of slaves.

The Mayas and Aztecs made their drink, which we know by
the Mexican name of *chocolatl,* by grinding the roasted cacao
beans and boiling them with ground maize and chili pepper. Before serving, the drink was frothed with a special stick, elab-
orately carved and with loose, wooden rings. It was served in
special ceremonial cups. The drink was thus very different from
our chocolate, which is an invention of the Spaniards who hit
upon the idea of mixing sugar with cacao. (Sugar as a product
of cane or bamboo seems to have got left out of this tropical
food discussion; sugar cane originated in peninsular India, but it
was among the first plants to be introduced into America by the
Spaniards.)

It is curious that cacao, which was so highly prized in the Mayan area, was unknown to the Andean civilizations of South America, who got their stimulation from chewing the leaves of a very different plant with a similar name, coca. Cacao is now an important export crop in Ecuador and Peru, and the Incas would presumably have adopted it had they known of it. The absence of cacao from the Andean region, like the absence of hieroglyphic writing, is one of the strong reasons for supposing that the two centers of civilization were quite independent.

Coffee, tea and chocolate interest us especially because they are the three drinks widely used in the Western world that came originally from the tropics. Beside these, there are numerous drinks that have never "caught on" outside some particular culture, like the maté of the Paraguay Indians. On the face of it, maté would seem to me as likely to spread as tea or coffee, yet it has never been widely adopted outside of the limited region of South America where it was used by the Indians, though in this area it seems to hold its own easily.

From these drinks, of course, it is an easy step to the narcotics and stimulants that are chewed or inhaled, things like betel nut, coca and tobacco. Even opium and hemp might be brought in as gifts of the tropics to help man in his efforts to escape from reality, though opium is one of those borderline Asiatic things that may have got started either inside or outside of the line of Cancer.

But the chief virtue of a survey of these drinks and drugs would be to show the extraordinary variety of tropical products that man has learned to use or misuse. And this in turn is but a manifestation of the tremendous variety of tropical nature itself, which I think warrants examination in a separate chapter.

★

CHAPTER XI

Tropical Nature

I N the center of Antarctica, where water is always ice, life
is impossible under present climatic conditions, because
life as we know it is dependent on water in liquid form. It
might be said that life is an aqueous solution, and much living
behavior is understandable only in terms of the behavior of the
solvent, water. On the fringes of Antarctica, a few mosses and
lichens are able to survive the almost continuous cold to take
advantage of the brief periods when air temperatures are above
freezing. In the Antarctic seas where water remains liquid
(though salty), life becomes abundant enough and even supports
a few terrestrial animals (like penguins) able to use this food
source and to generate their own internal heat, thus achieving
a measure of independence from climatic control.

In the "temperate" latitudes, water is ice for part of the year,
and all of the organisms that live in these latitudes must find
some method of surviving this recurrent physical calamity. The
majority of individuals (insects, annual plants and so forth) die,
though the species itself survives in the form of spores, seeds or
eggs in which the life processes are suspended for the duration
of winter, to be renewed with the rebirth of individuals in the
spring. In other cases the organism survives winter through some
special modification of its physiological processes, like trees

dropping their leaves or insects going into hibernation. In birds and mammals, the individual organism has achieved a considerable control of its internal temperature, so that activity can continue even though, in the outside world, all of the water has become ice.

But in every case survival through this unfavorable period when water is ice requires some shift in the ordinary business of living and growing and reproducing, some change in the nature and rate of the metabolic processes. With land organisms, then, it is only in those parts of the tropics where water, as water, is always freely available—as in the rain forest areas—that the business of living can be pursued unvaryingly throughout the year. Thus it is no wonder that terrestrial life has achieved its maximum complexity, its greatest diversity, under these conditions. This might be looked upon as the ideal, or "optimum," circumstance for terrestrial life.

I made a few remarks in Chapter VI on tropical vegetation types, in connection with the discussion of tropical climates. There I emphasized the fact that the nature of tropical vegetation depends primarily on the amount and annual distribution of the rainfall, except in mountainous regions where elevation (with resulting temperature changes) makes for added complications. I do not think the general subject of the classification of vegetation types, interesting and important though it is, needs further discussion in this book. The rain forest itself, however, warrants a special chapter—a book on the tropics without a discussion of the "jungle" would be unthinkable. Life in the tropical seas also needs separate treatment, since the conditions of life in the sea differ greatly from those of life on land.

In the present chapter, then, I shall try to point out a few general characteristics of tropical nature, and to touch on some of the more outstandingly peculiar groups of plants and animals. The following chapter will be given over to the special case of the rain forest, and the chapter after that to a brief discussion of tropical seas. Then we shall get back to man again by looking at these forests and seas as "resources" to be exploited or conserved, destroyed or enjoyed.

As I have so often said, the outstanding characteristic of tropical life is diversity. Almost all of the known kinds of living animals and plants are found in the tropics—using "kind" not in the sense of "species," but in the sense of a conspicuously marked group, family, order or class. Thus we think of conifers —pines, spruces and firs—as typical of the north, but there are great pine forests in Honduras. We tend to think of penguins as associated with icebergs off Antarctica, but there are penguins around the Galapagos Islands on the equator. Polar bears, to be sure, are limited to the north, but there are several kinds of tropical bears.

I wrote "almost" to be on the safe side, because there are surely many exceptions. The ones I think of now are geographical curiosities. New Zealand, for instance, is entirely outside of the tropics, yet because of its isolated position and relatively genial climate, various types of organisms have survived there long after they became extinct everywhere else. There is, for instance, the peculiar lizard called Sphenodon, which is the only living representative of a kind of reptile that was common everywhere in past geological ages. And then, of course, there is that peculiar bird, the kiwi. There are no kiwis in the tropics, nor anywhere except in New Zealand.

Aside from special cases like New Zealand, I think these living fossils are more apt to linger on in the tropics than elsewhere, though I have not worked up any statistics on the matter. Thus to counterbalance the Sphenodon and the kiwi, we have things like the dragon lizards of Komodo in the East Indies; and the duck-billed Platypus and the egg-laying Echidna of New Guinea; the sloths of South America; the odd little shrew-like Solenodon of Cuba; and a long list of queer things in places like Madagascar and other isolated parts of the forested tropics.

In contrast to the skimpy list of groups of animals and plants that are exclusively or characteristically arctic or boreal, we have the interminable list of groups that are exclusively or characteristically tropical. Most of them, unfortunately, have no common English names (since English is a boreal rather than a tropical language), which hampers discussion. But I could indicate the general trend of such a list by starting off with palms, monkeys, hummingbirds, sloths, parrots, bamboos, crocodiles, elephants— though some of these have a few species that stray out of the tropics.

The tropical region is not only rich in different types of organisms; it is also very rich in species. Statistics on this point are not easy to come by, because scientists are a long way from finishing the job of cataloguing species in the tropics. Among insects, a good proportion of the specimens that one collects in any tropical forest will turn out to be "new to science"; and even the forest trees often turn out to be undescribed. Birds are better known than most other animals, and my friend Theodosius Dobzhansky has collected the following statistics on these: Greenland has 56 breeding species; Labrador, 81; Newfoundland, 118; New York, 195; Florida, 143; Guatemala, 469; Panama, 1100; Colombia, 1395; Venezuela, 1148; the Lower Amazon, 738.

There are many species, many different kinds of things, in the tropics; but this usually means that no single kind of thing is very common. Thus a tropical forest may have about the same number of trees per acre as a northern forest; but the northern forest will consist of one kind of tree, or three or four kinds of trees, while in the tropical forest almost every tree will be different. Dobzhansky made some counts of this on the Amazon. In one place, in one hectare (2½ acres) of forest, he found 564 trees of 60 different kinds. In another place, in one hectare, he found 423 trees of 87 different kinds.

Great swarms of a single kind of insect, or herds of a single kind of mammal, are more characteristic of northern regions than of the tropics. Of course there are large herds on the African savannahs, but these include a whole series of different species of antelopes; while the grazing on our North American plains was monopolized by one animal, the bison. In a tropical forest, almost every insect that you collect will be different, almost every bird that you see will be new for the day. The end result is that the tropical naturalist gets swamped in this diversity, so that it takes a real effort of will to concentrate on any one thing, to study the habits of a particular bird or butterfly. The tendency is to keep on collecting, to keep on marveling at the new things that each day brings.

This very diversity often disappoints visitors who expect to see monkeys hanging from every tree, brilliant birds lurking in every bush, or gaudy flowers neatly massed against a verdant background. The variety of different kinds of things means that each particular thing must be looked for. One day you may come across a band of monkeys; the next day, perhaps, you will find some magnificent orchids and see a pair of macaws. Each kind of thing must be looked for and appreciated separately. Mass effects are exceptional, save for the rather gloomy and oppressive grandeur of the forest itself.

Tropical gardens, to be sure, are usually very colorful; and I think this has led us to associate bright flowers with the tropics. Most of the garden plants are hardly different from their wild relatives; but in the garden things from all over the world have been assembled and massed, while in the wild the separate plants are diluted in the overwhelming mass of green.

The scarcity of conspicuous flowers in the wild was brought home to me in Colombia when I tried color photography. It took patience, time and luck to find patches of color to contrast with the green vegetation and blue sky. Eventually, I learned to use props. For roadside scenes, a bright red pick-up truck owned by the laboratory was very useful. For forest pictures, I got both human interest and color by getting the lab boys to wear bright red kerchiefs on their heads, making a nice contrast with their blue jeans, and brown naked torsos.

The garden effects are achieved with shrubs, vines and trees—annual plants are rarely used in tropical gardens. Many things, like bougainvilleas and hibiscus, will bloom all of the year, so that color is always present. The trees are more apt to have a definite flowering season; and when massed they may produce spectacular effects. One of my most vivid memories of Egypt is of the colors of the flowering trees that lined the streets in the Cairo suburb of Ma'adi, where we lived. The poincianas would all be flaming red at one time in the spring; the jacarandas, at a slightly different date, would be solid blue; and along with these were the bauhinias which, for a few weeks, would be blanketed with their lavender, orchid-like flowers.

In the forest itself, nothing is seen of these flowering trees except the occasional patches of fading flowers that have dropped to mould among the litter of dead leaves. Only on mountain slopes can one get a view of what is happening. I once lived for a couple of years in Honduras in a narrow mountain valley where the slopes were covered with heavy forest. There I could watch the changing colors of the forest canopy as different trees and vines came into flower. But this seemed part of the mountain landscape, rather than a property of the vegetation. The flowers themselves were remote and unidentifiable; their color was a detail in a view that was always grand.

Of course the beauty and interest of tropical vegetation by no means depends on flowers alone. There are also the elements of form and foliage; and in this connection palms at once come to mind.

Palms have aptly been called the "princes of plants." They are, by any criterion, graceful and beautiful things. This is true of the curved informal coconuts that build the backdrop of white coral beaches everywhere on tropic seas. It is true of the formal, stately royal palms, whether in straight rows guarding an avenue, or rising disdainfully above some tangle of cutover tropical brush. It is true of the incredibly slender Euterpes that wave their delicate plumes above the massive forests that shut in the South American rivers. Palms, it seems to me, are quite fitting symbols for the tropics. They are useful, comfortable, strong and beautiful—but intolerant of cold.

There are about 1500 different species of palms, and they occur almost everywhere in the tropics, though the greatest profusion of species is in the East Indies and interior South America. Comparatively few are native outside of the tropics: a few kinds of palmetto in Florida and the Gulf States; Washingtonias in the American southwest; date palms and fan palms in the Mediterranean. But these stragglers are a mere handful compared with the wealth of tropical forms.

The palms are monocotyledonous plants—which means that they belong with the grasses, rushes and lilies. The trunk of a palm is more like a gigantic corn stalk than like the trunk of an ordinary tree. It has no bark, no cambium layer for the repair of wounds, no mechanism for growing in girth as it grows in height. This trunk is surmounted by a single tassel of gigantic leaves. In some species the leaves are fan-shaped and the biggest (Corypha) may be 15 feet in diameter; in others, the leaves are pinnate, and the longest (Maximiliana) may attain 50 feet.

Palms not only symbolize the tropics for outsiders; they have a very special importance for the local people. As the *Encyclopedia Britannica* points out, "They furnish food, shelter, clothing, timber, fuel, building materials, sticks, fibre, paper, starch, sugar, oil, wax, wine, tannin, dyeing materials, resin and a host of minor products, which render them most valuable to the natives." It is curious how many rural cultures are largely based on some particular type of palm—on the coconut palm in the East and West Indies, on the royal palm in Cuba, on the Moriche palm in the Upper Orinoco, on the date palm in parts of the Orient.

The leaves serve everywhere for thatch, the trunks for timber. The fruits of a few species are eaten directly by man (dates, coconuts, pejibaye) and those of other species are used for domestic animals, especially hogs (royal palm, moriche palm and so on). "Rattan" is the product of a curious climbing palm of the East whose stems may reach fantastic lengths—a thousand feet, according to Alfred Russel Wallace, making probably the "longest of all vegetable growths."

Palm wine ought to have special mention. Good quantities of a sweet sap can be collected from the cut flower stalks of several kinds of palms, and primitive man early learned that this, if allowed to ferment, resulted in a drink with the magical properties that always go with alcohol.

Another characteristic element in the tropical landscape is provided by the bamboos, which are giant grasses. They are less rigidly tropical than palms, since many species extend quite far north in Asia and can be grown in gardens all through the southern United States. They rival the palms, however, in their utility to tropical man.

Daryll Forde, writing of the use of bamboo by the Semang people of the forests of Malaya, remarks that "the pliancy and toughness of the wood, the sharpness of its cut edges and its tubular form adapt it for many uses, from cooking-vessels and arrow quivers to matting and knives. A fire-hardened blade of bamboo will cut ordinary bamboo itself and keep its edge for a considerable time."

The uses are greatly multiplied among more advanced cultures. Bamboo is often the basic building material for houses, or it may be used as scaffolding, ladders and beams in building houses of other materials. The cut stems, flattened out, make an excellent lath on which to apply plaster. Long stems are often used for water conduits, single joints for bottles, opened joints for dishes. The new shoots of many oriental species are eaten. We once made some attempts to eat the young shoots of the giant American bamboo, but we proved to our own satisfaction that they are incdiblc. Wc tried cooking them in many different ways, but our best result tasted rather like celluloid impregnated with castor oil.

Bamboo is apt to be used as an example of the rapid growth of vegetation in the tropics. This is not quite fair, because the whole bamboo plant is the "clump" and clumps are slow enough in establishing themselves, sending up increasingly large shoots over a period of years. But once the clump has become established, individual shoots certainly grow with extraordinary speed. I have sometimes stopped by a new bamboo shoot and watched it closely for a while, trying to see it grow, but without success. It is astonishing enough, though, to put a stake by the shoot and thus see the growth when you come back again a few hours later. The record seems to be held by a bamboo in Ceylon called Dendrocalamus giganteus, which has been observed to grow 16 inches in a day.

Palms and bamboos, of course, are not the only plants contributing to the special effects of tropical foliage. Tree ferns, where they occur, add a distinctive touch to the landscape, as do the many broad leaved, banana-like plants. And one of the most striking characteristics of tropical vegetation is the multiplicity of plants that grow on other plants.

I suppose that every scientist resident in the tropics has developed a special patter for explaining to visitors the difference between parasites and epiphytes, because almost invariably the visitor will call the orchids, air plants, ferns and so forth that he sees growing on trees "parasites." They are not parasites. A parasite is an organism that lives at the expense of another organism, depending on the host for essential food. These orchids and air plants simply use the trees on which they grow as perches, causing them no direct damage. The botanists call such plants epiphytes.

Mosses and lichens grow on trees as epiphytes in temperate

latitudes, but they are skimpy representatives indeed of the luxuriant epiphytic growth of the tropics. There are all kinds of plants among the epiphytes, but perhaps the commonest are ferns, orchids, bromeliads, peppers, cacti and aroids. They occur most abundantly in the rain forest and in the cloud forests of mountains, but they are found in all sorts of other situations, even in semiarid country.

The epiphytic habit poses some special biological problems, since the plants must grow in the absence of soil. They build up starch, like all green plants, from the carbon dioxide of the air; but they differ from most plants in that they cannot get minerals and water from the earth. They usually have strong root systems, which anchor them firmly to the bark on which they grow; and usually these root systems have a symbiotic relationship with fungi, which gather minerals and other nutrients from the traces that occur in rain water trickling over the bark. Water itself, of course, must be carefully conserved and stored by the plant, since intermittent rains are the only source of supply. The "bulbs" of orchids serve this purpose, as do the "tanks" of air plants.

I think the air plants, or bromeliads, can more appropriately be discussed in the next chapter in connection with the rain forest; but it may be a good idea to insert a few words about orchids here, since the visitor to the tropics is often disappointed about orchids, as he is about wild flowers in general.

There are many thousands of kinds of orchids in the tropics, and the plants, in a great many places, are extremely abundant. But most of these have small and inconspicuous flowers, hardly likely to be noticed except by the naturalist. The gaudy ones are there all right, but they have to be looked for, and they generally turn up hopelessly out of reach, high in the forest canopy. The best way to collect them is to be around when someone is clearing forest, so that they can be removed from the newly felled trees.

Most of our hothouse orchids are kinds that grow wild in the mountain forests, at five or six thousand feet, where the clouds make a pretty continuous fog. Epiphytes of all kinds grow luxuriantly in such forests, and the trees sometimes seem completely

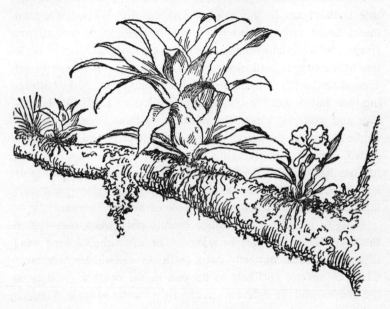

Plants Growing as Epiphytes.

smothered under the load of mosses, ferns, bromeliads and orchids. Cloud forest is not included on the ordinary tourist itinerary, because it has usually been cut over in the accessible places, near highways or cities. The cloud forests that I know are all on tortuous and muddy trails that must be negotiated by mule or on foot; but the landscape is worth the effort, in mule-days, required to reach it.

But the tropical life does not consist of plants only. There are also the animals that eat the plants, or that eat the animals that have eaten the plants, and we cannot make a survey of tropical nature without some attention to these animals. You can find insects no matter where you are in the tropics, unless it be in an absolute desert; so they should make a good starting point.

No one has the slightest idea how many different kinds of insects there are in the tropics. Guesses for the world's total insect fauna range anywhere from one million to ten million species, with the latter figure much more probable. Most of these live in the tropics, and most are still waiting for scientists to get around to the job of naming and describing them, and of studying their habits and life histories. Conspicuous kinds like butterflies and annoying kinds like mosquitoes have been pretty well studied even in the upper Amazon, central Africa or interior New Guinea; but the teeming mass of proletarian tropical insect life has hardly been dented by the few thousand entomologists who have been diligently collecting, pinning, describing and storing their specimens for the last couple of hundred years.

Most of us, of course, notice insects only when they fall in the soup, when they bite or sting us, or when the flashing wing of some metallic butterfly calls forth an astonished "oh my!" These things are all likely to happen in the north as well as in the tropics, and the difference is chiefly a matter of scale. Metallic colors, for instance, are rare in northern butterflies and common in tropical ones, reaching a maximum in the giant Morphos whose six or eight-inch wings are, in many species, solid, dazzling, metallic blue. This frequency of metallic coloration among tropical insects must have some easy explanation. There are bright, metallic mosquitoes, too, some of them with tufts of gaudy red scales by way of contrast, and with these I have thought that the color was an adaptation to life in the high temperatures and low humidities of tropical sunlight, a mechanism whereby the heat was reflected from the insect's body instead of being absorbed. But such an explanation carries less weight in the case of the Morpho butterflies, because the metallic coloration is chiefly a male characteristic, the females being rather dowdy insects. To be sure, gaudiness is generally a male attribute under tropical conditions—or any other conditions for that matter.

Butterflies are conspicuous insects in most parts of the tropics. Along a forest trail, they usually provide a much larger element of color in the landscape than do the flowers. There are dull colored butterflies too, and in deep forest these may be the most abundant, flitting about over the debris of the forest floor. Some of these forest butterflies have completely transparent wings, giving a ghostly effect that fits well with the general gloom.

There are endless topics that might be discussed in connection with tropical insects. Among them, one can find examples of almost all known kinds of animal behavior, including kinds of behavior that are not shown by anything else. There are the leaf-cutting ants with their subterranean gardens in which they carefully cultivate fungi on the bits of leaves that they drag into their nests along their busy forest highways. There are the stinging ants that live in the hollow stems or hollow thorns of various trees like Cecropia, Triplaris and Acacia, where it looks as though the tree provided special accommodations for the ants (sometimes including special food nectaries) in return for the protection given by the agile warriors. Then there are the termites with their complex social habits, and their efficiently developed industry which rapidly removes all dead wood from the tropical scene.

These tropical insects have a whole catalogue of tricks for escaping enemies; and the enemies, a correspondingly diverse variety of ways for catching their prey. Here mimicry reaches its greatest perfection. Mimicry is the trick whereby a moth or other defenseless insect comes to look like a wasp; or a tasty butterfly comes to look like some other kind of butterfly that is protected from predators by an acrid secretion or suchlike device. Here also are found the extreme examples of protective coloration— bugs that look exactly like the spines of the plants on which they live; butterflies that copy dead leaves, complete with veins and mould spots and tattered margins; caterpillars that look like the dropping of a bird.

There are also, of course, centipedes and scorpions; and cockroaches that reach a size and proportion that makes them look like small mud turtles. These last do not do any great harm, but they take a certain amount of getting used to. And in the grasslands and forest there are ticks, red-bugs, mosquitoes, and all sorts of other things that bite, sting, burn or itch. But I've read somewhere that in the Canadian woods, there is something called a blackfly. . . . And did I hear someone mention the New Jersey marshes?

Insects in the tropics have their uses, too, in that they provide an element of variety in the tropical diet. Since I neglected to mention them in the chapter on "Food and Drink," perhaps a few supplementary notes should be inserted here. Charles Brues, who has written a review of the subject, points out that insects "fall mainly into the class of delicacies so far as human consumption is concerned." Thus in Siam there is a giant water bug called Lethocerus which is steamed and then picked like a lobster; the meat is said to have a strong flavor, reminiscent of Gorgonzola cheese. It is used, dried and pulverized, to add zest to curries, or combined with shrimps, lime juice, garlic and pepper, to make a popular sauce called "namphla." A similar use of certain stinkbugs in Mexico has been described, though the famous insect element of Mexican diet is the larva of a giant grub which, when toasted, makes a delicate hors d'oeuvre. Giant beetle grubs are, in fact, very widely used in the tropics as a food delicacy, as are toasted ants or termites.

You shudder, yet you have no hesitancy in stabbing a cringing oyster, pulling it from the shell, bathing it in a tomato sauce, and inserting it between the teeth. When eating oysters, I often think of Samuel Butler's remark that if oysters squealed, people would not eat them alive; but they do not squeal, and I enjoy them as much as the next fellow. What is the difference between oysters, shrimp, snails, water bugs and beetle grubs?

The difference, of course, is not between oysters and beetle grubs. It is between the culture, the training, the conditioning of the people who eat them. I remember once explaining to a friend, who was sharing a dish of toasted ants with me, that in my country people ate frogs. My friend was horrified.

But that is enough about insects. The next topic probably ought to be snakes, which I think for many people symbolize the dreadful connotations of the tropics, as palms symbolize the romantic connotations. The palm association, I think, is justified, but not the snake association. There are more different kinds of snakes in the tropics than anywhere else, but the increase in numbers of kinds is not so startling as with some other sorts of organisms. There are, for instance, 22 different species of snakes known from Canada, 126 from the United States, 293 from Mexico, and 210 from Brazil.

I am scared of snakes, I suspect because I was brought up in southern Florida at a time and place where rattlesnakes were common enough to be a real danger, so that my father rightly trained me to be always wary and on the lookout. But despite the fact that most of my life has been spent in the tropics, I can report no snake adventures; and I tend to raise my eyebrows when I read about such in travel books. I remember an account in a book on Brazil, where the author while climbing a tree had a narrow escape from a deadly snake. Unfortunately, none of the deadly Brazilian snakes can climb. To find one in a tree would be like finding a copperhead while climbing a dooryard maple in New England. There are plenty of arboreal snakes in Brazil, but none with striking fangs. In Central America, there is a palm viper—a beautiful green thing that I would hate to encounter while tree climbing—but it does not get as far south as Brazil.

I used to wear high boots or leather puttees in the tropical forest, as a precaution against snake bite; and I must admit that I feel more comfortable about snakes with such gear on. But I have long since abandoned this protection in favor of shorts and sandals because the boots, in every other respect, are a damned nuisance. I take comfort in the statistics which show, in general, that more people die from being hit by lightning than from snake bite. An exception, of course would be India, but the mortality statistics there result from a combination of factors: the habits of cobras, the superstition of the people, and the low incidence of footwear of any kind.

There are comparatively few species of poisonous snakes in tropical America—none at all on the large islands of the West Indies. There are many more kinds in tropical Africa and Asia, and in Australia most of the snakes are poisonous.

Popular interest in tropical snakes involves not only the venomous kinds, but also the constrictors: the pythons of the Old World and the boas of America. The regal python of Malaya has the record for length—up to 33 feet. The anaconda or water boa of the upper Amazon is not so long (the record is 25 feet) but it is a much thicker snake, so that a big anaconda would outweight a big python. Either one is terrifying enough, and I do not wonder that people are afraid of them, but attacks on man must be very rare. The usual food is much smaller game.

Snakes ought to be tropical animals, because they have little control over their body temperature; and when cold weather comes, they have to go out of commission until it warms up again. But I think that birds, despite their efficient control of body temperature, are essentially more tropical than snakes. There are many birds in the gardens, hedgerows and woods of places like England and Connecticut. But most of these, quite sensibly, head south about the time of the first frost.

Apparently this is more a matter of food supply than it is of temperature. Birds, with their ceaseless activity, require a lot of food. Many of them depend on insects and fruit, and when this supply fails with the onset of winter, they start out for places where insects and fruit can still be found. At least this seems to be the basis of the migration habit. The actual controlling mechanism, of course, may be quite different, depending on some environmental factor like the changing length of day.

The migrating birds are but a small fraction of the total bird population of the tropics. Yet, as I mentioned earlier, the traveler to the tropics should not expect too much, because these birds are not as obvious in the wild as they are in a zoological garden. As Alfred Russel Wallace has pointed out, "although the number of brilliantly-colored birds in almost every part of the tropics is very great, yet they are by no means conspicuous, and as a rule they can hardly be said to add much to the general effect of the equatorial scenery. The traveler is almost always disappointed at first with the birds, as he is with the flowers and the beetles; and it is only when, gun in hand, he spends days in the forest, that he finds out how many beautiful living things are concealed by its dense foliage and gloomy thickets."

Mammals, of course, are much harder to find than birds, and in the forest one rarely comes across anything except monkeys; and the monkeys, in a region where there is much hunting, are not apt to stay in sight for long. The veldt country of Africa is the great exception to this generalization about mammals, and the Kruger National Park, which is crossed by the Tropic of Capricorn in South Africa, must be the most marvellous place in the world for observing big game.

Most mammals, even the forest ones, rapidly become less shy of man if they are protected from hunting; but there are few places in the tropics where such protection exists. One such is the small island called Barro Colorado, in Gatun Lake in the Panama Canal Zone. A biological laboratory was established there in 1923, and hunting has been strictly prohibited since that date. I once spent six months there, and I saw more wild mammals during that time than in all of my years of wandering in other parts of the American tropics. The tapirs and big cats remain shy, but the others become relatively indifferent to human beings, so that they can easily be observed as they go about their daily business.

People (including naturalists) are more interested in monkeys than in any other group of mammals. This is true of monkeys in a zoo, and it is even more true of monkeys in their native forests. In a place like Barro Colorado where there is no hunting, the monkeys return the compliment. As Frank Chapman wrote, "Quite obviously we arouse in them an intense curiosity. . . . There is something in the Howler's steady, intent stare, in the efforts of the Capuchin to obtain a nearer and a better view, in the Night Monkey's peering, and the Marmoset's awareness that warrants the belief we are something more to them than merely large, strange creatures."

I was supposed to be collecting butterflies while I was on Barro Colorado but, as I wandered along the trails, I was always getting distracted by the temptation to watch the monkeys. The Howlers were the most fun because, by hurling a few insults at them, you could always get them stirred up into making a rousing reply. As Chapman says, "A Howler chorus is one of the most impressive sounds in the animal world. When you are its cause, and a bearded old male Howler with the face of a satyr climbs down threateningly toward you, every tooth revealed as he roars, it requires some self-persuasion to hold your ground."

The Howlers have a sort of "loud speaker" which is essentially an enormous distention of the hyoid bone into a large, deep cup which lies between the lower jaws, and which contains part of the larynx. This results in an increase in resonance rather like that obtained by blowing across the mouth of a bottle. A band of howling Howlers can be heard for miles, and I never fail to get a thrill out of listening to them as they greet the dawn.

There are 15 different types (genera) of New World monkeys, and a similar number in the Old World, each distinctive not only in appearance but in character. And in the Old World there are, in addition, the great apes—the chimpanzees and gorillas of Africa and the orangutans and gibbons of the Asiatic tropics. They are all tropical, which would justify us in going on with monkey stories here. But there is no need, because Earnest Hooton has covered the ground completely in his book on *Man's Poor Relations*. To anyone who wants an introduction to the world of monkeys and apes, I can only recommend that they look up Hooton.

These primates are not only tropical; they are almost all essentially inhabitants of that most fascinating of tropical environments, the rain forest, which is the subject of the next chapter.

CHAPTER XII

★

The Rain Forest

I FIRST encountered the rain forest when, fresh out of college, I went to Honduras to work for the United Fruit Company. I was supposed to be studying the diseases of bananas, and I spent my work days faithfully counting fungus spots or writing company memoranda, or watching the black bees that nicked the margins of the banana fingers in the course of their curious sap-collecting operations. But on holidays I headed for the forest. Our experimental station was located in a valley back from the port of Tela, where the vegetation had been preserved to protect the town water suply. The rainfall was about two hundred inches a year, which meant that the hills at the head of the valley were covered with a magnificent forest where a young naturalist could find all sorts of interesting things.

I wasn't able to carry out any systematic studies on this holiday schedule and presently I was transferred to the highlands of Guatemala for quite different sorts of work in a very different environment. After that came a stretch of years in the Intemperate environment of Cambridge, Massachusetts, which was broken by a few tantalizing vacation excursions into the tropics; then a four-year period chasing mosquitoes in the Mediterranean region. The memory of that Honduras experience, however, remained undimmed and I kept up the hope of finding some practical way to get back to the tropical forest to carry out systematic studies. This hope was finally fulfilled when the Rockefeller Foundation suggested that I take up mosquito studies in connection with the problem of jungle yellow fever.

A friend, who had visited the yellow fever laboratory at Villa-vicencio in eastern Colombia, described it to me and made it sound ideal. It had all of the proper and necessary laboratory equipment, and yet was located across the Andes on the margin of the great forest of interior South America: one of the most interesting parts of the world to the naturalist, and yet one of the least known because of the difficulties of travel and residence, and the unavailability of scientific equipment. These difficulties had been overcome because of the need of getting information about yellow fever. As far as I can see, the only nice thing about disease is that people get stirred up about it, so that they are willing to let scientists spend money in the hope of getting prac-tical results. The scientists get the practical results often enough to justify the practice, and at the same time they get a chance to add to the sum of human knowledge—an activity that in itself seems to have little appeal.

The Villavicencio laboratory turned out really to be ideal. We lived there for eight years, and during all of those years we knew that we were having the time of our lives; that we would never again find conditions so nearly perfect for a naturalist and a naturalist's wife. My wife wrote a book about it, which she called *East of the Andes and West of Nowhere,* so I won't repeat the story.

This experience, then, is the basis for the present chapter. It means that I am writing primarily about the equatorial American forest. The general characteristics of the African and Indonesian forests, however, are similar, though of course the plants and animals that play corresponding roles would be of different kinds.

This experience also means that my study of the forest was oriented around the problem of explaining the epidemiology of

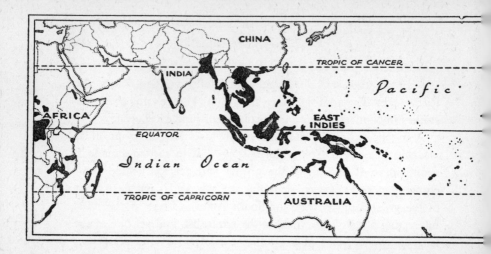

forest yellow fever. This turned out, however, to be an excellent guide through the maze of forest interrelationships. We eventually came to the conclusion that in our region the disease was maintained by epidemics among certain kinds of monkeys, and transmitted by a curious mosquito of a bright, metallic blue color, known by its scientific name of "Haemagogus." To understand this mosquito-monkey transmission, we had to study the habits of the mosquitoes and of the monkeys, and we soon found that we were led into all sorts of explorations of the forest environment, which I shall try to describe here.

The tropical rain forest is most commonly called "jungle," but I have never liked the word. It brings to mind snakes dripping from trees, panthers crouched in underbrush, centipedes crawling into boots. Explorers are always hacking their way through the "jungle"—but the ground, in the rain forest, is fairly open because the dense crowns of the big trees cut out so much light that few low-growing plants can survive.

There are all kinds of forests in the tropics and it is easy enough to find places that match the most fantastic Hollywood ideas. Some forests are so thick that it is almost impossible to get through them—second growth in a clearing made five or six years before, thickets of spiny bamboo, areas of swamp that

have been taken over by low-growing trees. But the typical rain forest, the great untouched forest of interior South America, is not like this. It is majestic rather than tangled; cathedral-like, with its dim light, narrowing vistas, great buttressed trunks and pervading silence.

I have seen many more snakes, poisonous or otherwise, in Florida than in South America. They are in the forest, all right, but they mostly stay pretty well hidden. I'd be scared to death if I ever encountered a jaguar in the forest, but I never have, though I have come across fresh-looking tracks often enough.

I cannot deny that there are insect pests. I am pretty much immune, which often led me to be thoughtless with visitors. My last visiting scientist was a victim of that. He showed an interest in my forests, and I dragged him all over the place without remembering to give him insect repellent (some of the repellents worked out by the army are good). He turned out to be very susceptible to red bugs—a tiny mite that anyone who has hunted in Florida knows well. He got covered with them, and the sores made him look as though someone had skinned him alive. After a week in bed, I shipped him off to the Gorgas Hospital in Panama. Apparently he had a very unusual sort of an allergic reaction to these mites, previously unknown to the annals of tropical medicine. This didn't comfort him any, though, and he refused to listen to further propaganda on my part.

As for diseases, very few are associated with the tropical forest. Most human diseases must pass directly from man to man, and they need a good supply of people for maintenance. The problem of disease in the tropics is a problem of villages, towns and cities, fostered more by poverty than by climate.

Yellow fever is an exception, because in the interior of South America it is a disease of monkeys as well as men, so that it might be caught in a remote and uninhabited forest. But the threat of yellow fever is gone for civilized man because of the efficient vaccine. There is no more danger from yellow fever today than there is from smallpox.

The scourge of the tropics is malaria, and most explorers have spent their days and weeks in shivering misery with the disease. The attacks may come on in camp far out in the forest, but I am sure the explorers got their malaria when they spent the night in a village on the way. The malaria mosquito does not fly very far, rarely more than a mile or so, and to transmit malaria it must, a week or so previously, have bitten someone infected with the parasite of the disease. The parasites that cause malaria in man can infect no other animal, so it remains a disease of villages and thickly settled farming regions.

But this is getting away from the subject of the rain forest. The "rain" part of the name is important. The nature of vegetation in the lowland tropics is controlled primarily by the amount and distribution of rainfall. A high rainfall, fairly evenly distributed through the twelve months, results in the most complex vegetation type, the rain forest. This means at least 150 inches of rain a year and usually 200 or more inches. For comparison, the precipitation in the eastern United States varies between 40 and 50 inches a year, being less than 40 over most of the central states. Tropical rainfalls are approached only in the Olympic Mountains of Washington, where the Wynoochee Oxbow station records 146 inches a year, the highest rainfall in the United States.

These sixteen or so annual feet of water fall in definite showers, "shower" in the sense of "shower bath." All-day, drizzling rains are uncommon. At first it bothered me to get soaked by one of these abrupt rains. But I found that the discomfort came mostly from the soggy clothes, and I eventually hit upon the scheme of taking all of my clothes off, carrying them in a waterproof bag during a rain. After the first cold shock, the bath was tolerable, and when the rain stopped the skin would dry off remarkably quickly and the clothes, scanty but required by local custom, could be put back on, dry. Waterproof coats, we found, were impossible because the clothes underneath would get soaked with sweat, if not by rain.

We started out, in our forest studies, by concentrating on the Haemagogus mosquitoes, because scientists in both Brazil and Colombia had suspected for some time that this might be the forest vector of yellow fever. At about the time of my arrival in Colombia, one of the yellow fever scientists, Dr. Jorge Boshell, discovered that these Haemagogus were most common in a forest when a tree had just been cut down. This seemed queer until he had the idea of climbing a tree before it was cut. It then turned out that the mosquitoes were always common in the tree-tops. It thus became clear that our first problem was to find out what was going on up in the tops of the trees in the forest.

We tried all sorts of methods of getting up into the trees. Climbing irons like those used by telephone linesmen and lumberjacks were among the first experiments. The climbing irons would have been fine if there had been no ants in the forest, but there must be about as many ants in one acre of tropical forest as in the whole United States. Some of them have stings that make our North American wasps seem sissies. I cannot brag about the Villavicencio snakes, but I'll back the ants against all comers.

It is rather awkward to come across a nest of these insects fifty feet up in a tree, with only climbing irons as support. You simply can't take your pants off and at the same time leave the belt fastened around the tree, and it becomes a matter of deciding between sudden death from the fifty-foot drop and slow torture with both ants and pants in place.

Actually, I never got as high as fifty feet with climbing irons, though some of my hardy colleagues have done much better. I preferred to pick a likely spot and have the laboratory carpenter make a ladder. He became expert at making twelve-foot lengths which he put in place up a trunk in no time at all. He learned how to build elegant platforms, from which the forest world could be viewed in peace and comfort. There you could take off your pants whenever necessary, remove and squash the ants, and resume contemplation—only slightly disturbed by a few itches, stings and burns.

I spent many happy hours in these forests, sometimes just sitting, sometimes trying to puzzle out the complex relations among the forest inhabitants, and sometimes about my proper business of making observations or collecting specimens. There is ample material for meditation. The rain forest and the coral reef must represent the maximum development of life on this planet, in that more different kinds of organisms and a larger number of individuals are packed into a given amount of space than in any other sort of situation. Both habitats provide the naturalist with inexhaustible material for study.

There are, as a matter of fact, many analogies between tropical forests and tropical seas. In both, the naturalist is always conscious of the third dimension, height or depth. We walk at the bottom of the forest and float on the top of the sea, and to explore this third dimension we have to use a deal of ingenuity in climbing or diving. But in both, the conditions of life gradually change from the bottom to the top in ways that are curiously parallel, resulting in a zoning by depth.

The zoning depends on the same basic factor in both cases—light. The light that strikes the surface of the sea diminishes rapidly with depth, so that the ocean floor is a region of perpetual darkness. Similarly, the light is cut by the dense foliage of the

Diagram to Show Rain Forest Structure (after Beard).

tropical forest. The forest floor region is not eternally dark, but the light is dim enough to exercise a selective influence on the kind of plants that can grow there.

The basic industry of photosynthesis is thus largely restricted to the canopy zone of the forest or to the surface region of the sea, and the organisms that live below depend in the long run on materials that drop down from above. The surface of the sea is inhabited by incredible millions of microscopic animals and plants, and there is a sort of constant rain of corpses of these organisms into the depths below, to serve as food supply for the bottom dwellers. Similarly, the inhabitants of the floor zone of the forest depend on the constant supply of dead leaves, of fallen fruits, flowers, branches and trunks, or on materials found in the soil.

The zoning of life in the sea is possible because of the density of water, which enables organisms to keep at whatever depth they prefer. Most organisms have just about the same density as sea water, so that swimming and floating are easy. Floating in the air, though, is a different thing, achieved only by very tiny organisms or by special arrangements like those of certain spiders that drift with long strands of silk. Flying, in contrast with swimming, is much harder work, so that no animal is able to live its whole life flying the way marine animals may live, always swimming or drifting with the current. The zoning in the forest depends on the trees, which form its basic structure, and getting to the top is a matter of climbing.

Tree growth itself is an adaptation for getting up in the air. It might be called "giantism." A tropical forest is composed of hundreds of different kinds of trees, many of them members of families that in the temperate zone include only shrubs or herbaceous plants. Thus bamboo is a grass that has become giant to get its share of forest light.

Other plants have developed the vine habit, using the giants as support to get to the top of the forest. Some of these vines become monstrous things, with thick, woody trunks—the lianas. The foliage at the top of the forest is made up of vine leaves as much as tree leaves, and it may be hard to tell which flowers and fruits belong to vines, and which to trees.

Perhaps the most interesting plant method of getting to the top of the forest is the epiphytic habit, which was discussed in the previous chapter.

Plants, then, get to the top of the forest through giantism, climbing or the epiphytic habit. Animals have to get there by climbing or flying, and climbing adaptations are consequently common in the forest fauna. Many mammals, for instance, have developed a prehensile tail, a tail that can be twisted around a branch and used for holding on, or even as a sort of fifth leg in swinging through the trees.

In South America there are several forest opossums with prehensile tails. There is an arboreal porcupine—a rodent—with a prehensile tail. The kinkajou, a carnivore related to the raccoon, has such a tail, as do certain anteaters, which belong to a very distinct order of mammals, the edentates. In some of the monkeys the tail has developed into a really marvellous organ, with the underside of the skin formed into sensitive palmar tissue. The tail of a spider monkey, for instance, is just as useful as its hand: and in investigating some object or other, a spider monkey seems not to feel satisfied until it has tested the thing with both its hands and its tail.

Now the curious thing is that this prehensile tail business is practically limited to South America. Only one mammal in all of the world outside of South America has such a tail—one of the Australian marsupials. If you see a monkey hanging by his tail, you can be sure that he is from tropical America, not from Africa or the Orient.

Mammals aren't the only animals with striking modifications for life in the forest. The Old World relatives of the domestic chicken are mostly ground birds, but in South America they have taken to the trees. There is a host of kinds of tree frogs, with highly developed sucker arrangements on their feet for sticking to branches and leaves. There are incredibly long and slim snakes, that look just like bits of the vines in which they spend their lives.

I think that the frequency of prehensile tails and other arboreal adaptations in tropical American animals reflects the ancientness of the tropical American forest. These great forests must have continued without interruption through long stretches of geological time, so that the most diverse animals and plants were slowly able to develop all sorts of complex ways of living together to form the forest habitat. Forests have of course existed for long times in other parts of the world, but not such vast forests, or for so long without interruptions by dry epochs in which the forest was replaced by grass.

When we found that the Haemagogus mosquitoes were predominantly "arboreal," despite their apparent freedom to fly at any level in the forest, we wanted to find out what sort of conditions led them to stay in the treetops. The first step was to find out how the climate differed at different heights in the forest, since it might be some climatic factor like temperature, humidity or light that kept the mosquitoes from flying near the ground. For this purpose, we established a series of stations at different heights in the trees where we could leave instruments for recording temperature, humidity and evaporation rate. We also kept records of temperature, humidity, light intensity and height above ground for all of our mosquito catches, so that the kind and number of mosquitoes caught could be related to these environmental factors.

It turned out that the forest climate was zoned. That is, conditions differed in a regular way from the ground to the top of the forest. The differences are most easily realized if we consider the extremes. In the open air, just above the forest canopy, there is no protection from sun and wind. Changes may be abrupt, the air warming rapidly when the sun rises in the morning and cooling rapidly after it sets. The temperature may drop several degrees in a few minutes with the onset of a rainstorm, and may vary considerably between cloudy and sunny periods.

Near the ground, in what I like to call the "forest floor zone," conditions are very different. The mass of foliage of the forest serves as an insulating agent, giving an effect comparable with that of a cork-lined room. It is a long time after the sun comes up in the morning before any change in air temperature occurs in this part of the forest, and the change then is very slow. The drop with nightfall is equally slow. Thus the air during most of the day is much cooler than the air in the open above the forest, while during the night it is warmer.

There is a comparable difference in humidity. It is always damp within the forest, and the air near the ground is saturated with moisture all day long. In the open, the air may become quite dry during the day, though it is usually saturated everywhere at night in the wet tropics. During the day, then, humidity in the forest is highest near the ground, and the air gradually becomes drier climbing toward the canopy; at night this humidity difference disappears. The temperature, during the day, is lowest near the forest floor, the air becoming warmer higher up; while at night this change may be reversed. Mixing of the air is limited because the dense foliage cuts out wind, and slows up all air currents. There is, of course, a similar change in light, from the bright sun above the forest to the dense shade near the ground. Here the change is similar at night, since the light is always brightest above the forest.

We never did arrive at a clear-cut explanation of the factors that kept the Haemagogus mosquitoes high in the forest. I thought that probably humidity was important, since they showed a tendency to avoid very moist air like that near the forest floor. Light also may have been important; and some of our laboratory experiments indicated that there may have been some sort of a visual factor. At least the mosquitoes in a large cage would stay near the top of the cage, even when humidity, temperature and light were the same at the top and bottom.

The forest studies turned out to be most important in connection with our laboratory studies with yellow fever virus. To keep our Haemagogus alive for transmission experiments, we found that we had to keep them in a fairly dry cabinet, provided with a fan to produce air currents. To get the virus established in the mosquitoes, we had to expose them to relatively high temperatures for a while each day. All of these things—low humidity, presence of air movement, periodic high temperature—were characteristics of the forest canopy, not of the forest floor zone. The mosquitoes and the virus (as well, of course, as the monkeys) thus appeared to be linked to environmental conditions of the treetop region of the forest.

I might note that the zoning of temperature in the forest fits my analogy between the forest and the sea, as does the zoning in light. In the sea, temperatures also vary most at the surface, becoming increasingly constant with depth. There is also an analogy between wind action and wave action, which are strongest at the surface in both the forest and the sea. Humidity, of course, is not a factor in the sea. This makes things a lot easier for the marine biologist, because humidity is one of the more difficult environmental factors to study and control.

From man's point of view there is one big difference between the forest and the sea: we can float on top of the sea, but we have to walk along the bottom of the forest. I have often wished I had some way of collecting all of the lovely insects that must be buzzing around in the top of the forest, or some way of getting up to measure the temperature or watch the monkeys in the uppermost branches. I think it is easier to dive than to climb— maybe because I have done more climbing than diving.

The South American forest also resembles a sea in size. It is not vast like the Pacific Ocean, but it is as extensive as most seas —the Caribbean, for instance. The whole upper Amazon is a great continuous forest, from Venezuela and Colombia down through Bolivia. It divides into gulfs and bays along its northern limits, with long fingers that extend into the savannah country. There are outlying seas in the mountain valleys, in Central America, and in many parts of Brazil.

In this modern age you can fly over the forest, and when you have watched the unbroken canopy for a few hours from a comfortable seat in an air liner, you begin to realize how big this forest is. The explorers, who spent weeks and months traversing its rivers, paddled by uncertain Indians in their uncertain canoes, must have realized the vastness of the forest even more clearly. There is still no way of traveling long distances through the forest except by water. As a result, the country away from the major rivers is almost unknown, probably the least known part of the earth outside of the polar regions.

From the earliest days naturalists have commented on the wealth of different kinds of plants and animals found in the forests. No catalogue has ever been made of all of the organisms in any South American forest, so it is impossible to give exact statistics. Scientists have been visiting the patch of rain forest on Barro Colorado Island in the Panama Canal Zone for many years now, and the forest there is probably more completely known than any other. Yet every visitor finds new things.

We found about 150 different kinds of mosquitoes within a radius of five miles of the Villavicencio laboratory—more kinds than have been found in all of the United States. Yet mosquitoes were not especially noticeable. During the war, we made experiments at the request of the army with many different chemicals, trying to find something that would give mosquito protection under tropical conditions. Parallel experiments were being conducted in the New Jersey salt marshes, and the army sent me the results of the New Jersey experiments, asking me to try to use the same methods as far as possible. I found, however, that this was impossible. They were getting sixty mosquito bites a minute in New Jersey, and the best we could do in our tropical forest was sixty bites an hour. We had ten times as many different kinds of mosquitoes in a particular experiment as they had in New Jersey, but they had sixty times as many individual mosquitoes!

To understand this tremendous diversity of kinds of plants and animals, it is necessary to think in terms of what the naturalist calls "niches." The tropical forest is full of niches, and life in each particular niche is carried on more or less independently. Take the matter of zonation. The organisms high in the forest canopy, those low in the canopy, those that live on the ground and those that live under the ground, all carry on pretty much independently of each other. And each of these major zones is full of nooks and crannies each occupied by its special kinds of animals and plants.

The mosquitoes again furnish a useful example. The larvae of all mosquitoes live in water, and my favorite method of looking for new species was to go out into the forest and try to think of some new place where water might accumulate. If I found a new sort of place with water, I almost invariably found some new kind of mosquito larva living there. Obvious places were rotholes in trees, and the water collected by the air plants, or bromeliads. Less obvious was the water that collected in the internodes of bamboo where a bird or beetle had made a hole in the stem; the water that collected in certain kinds of large upright flowers; the thin film of water at the base of the leaves of many banana-like plants. Nothing like as many different kinds of places holding water could be found in any temperate forest.

The air plants, or bromeliads, are a good example of a "niche." I have mentioned these several times in connection with the epiphytic habit, because most of them are epiphytes, though a few, like the pineapple, grow on the ground. The bromeliads mostly have long, narrow leaves that grow from a common center, where the bases of the leaves form a sort of watertight vessel which the botanists call a "tank." A lot of water may accumulate in a large plant—sometimes several quarts. Dead leaves, twigs and other bits of forest debris accumulate in the plant along with the water, making a rich infusion that serves as a source of food for the plant. The water of the tank, in turn, becomes "home" to a whole special fauna and flora: bacteria, fungi, microscopic animals, worms, snails, insect larvae of many kinds (including mosquitoes) and the tadpoles of certain kinds of tree frogs. The whole thing is like a tiny pond perched on the branch of a tree high in the forest.

Thus the forest as a whole, with its niches and niches within niches, becomes a sort of multiplication table of possibilities for different kinds of life. The abundance of food and water, the even distribution of sunlight, make the growth of many kinds of trees possible. The diversity of trees offers opportunity to a diversity of hangers-on. Each of these in turn has its parasites or symbionts, or provides new kinds of food or shelter for ever more kinds of organisms. The niches and the animals and plants able to use them thus multiply to dizzy figures.

Much has been written about the "struggle for existence" in the tropical forest. It is easy to believe this when you see a tree smothered with vines, when you see how every leaf and every fruit has been eaten by something, when you think of all of the animals busily hunting each other in search of their daily meals. But there is also something wrong with the idea of this struggle. If the struggle is so keen, how does it come that so many different kinds of things have managed to survive? Many of the animals and plants of the South American forests are clearly very ancient types, types that have died out everywhere else in the world, though we know they were once more widely spread because of the fossil record.

Apparently conditions in the forest are so favorable that almost anything can survive, and almost everything does. Individuals may have a hard time, but some of them seem always to manage to leave offspring; and no one kind of animal or plant is able to get the upper hand of all of the rest, and thus dominate the landscape.

Even man has not succeeded in dominating the South American forests, though he has made great inroads on their margins. The conservatism of the forest seems to affect the humans, too. The Motilone Indians of Colombia are still as hostile and as unconquered as when they faced the first conquistadores, and the same is true of some of the Brazilian tribes. The forest Indians have probably never been really numerous, probably never achieved any very high level of culture. Yet they have managed to resist the impact of Western civilization more completely than any other people. It is as though they were affected by the inertia of the forest, the same forest character that protects ancient animal types long after they have become extinct in other parts of the world.

The Mayas of Central America seem to be the only people who have responded to the challenge of the forest, who have conquered the forest and built up a civilization from its elements. But their history is so lost in the nebulous past that we cannot be sure how they did this, or whether their civilization really had its genesis in the forest, or moved there from some other sort of environment.

It is surprising how little this forest has to offer civilized man. There are valuable timber trees, but they are difficult to exploit because the valuable trees are scattered and lost among the host of sorts for which man has no particular use. There are fruits and fibers and medicinal plants, but again the kinds that man wants are almost hopelessly diluted in the mass of forest vegetation.

The soil seems tremendously rich to support this great forest, yet attempts to bring it under cultivation have not been outstandingly successful. The whole forest is a delicate balance, and if it is cleared, the thin accumulation of topsoil may be washed away with the rains of next year. Or the growth of weeds may be so fast and so dense that the crop is smothered. Local peoples everywhere have the custom of cutting forest, burning it, getting a crop or two before the weeds get out of control, and then abandoning the spot to the processes of nature. After five or ten or fifty years, it may be ready to cut and burn again. To keep the soil under control seems beyond their power, or their ambition.

To what extent the forest could be brought under control, could be used for human settlement, is a matter of much debate among the experts. The job surely will not be easy, else it would have been finished long ago. Probably it will require detailed scientific study, the adoption of special methods that will enable man to compete with and to control the natural processes that govern the development of the forest itself.

This could be a very interesting study, but I rather hope it fails. Civilized man has got completely used to lording it over the landscape, turning everything into neat orchards and fields, or dismal wastes of cutover second growth. It is a humbling experience, and surely a healthy one, to enter a landscape that man has not been able to alter, to dominate, to twist to his own purposes. Man in the rain forest is just another rather simple animal, walking quietly and apprehensively, scared at the snapping of a branch, not sure where he will find his next meal. He gains a new perspective in this complex world which he has not yet been able even to catalogue, let alone control. It is not a hostile world, but it is very indifferent to human needs and human purposes.

CHAPTER XIII

★

Tropical Seas

SEVENTY-EIGHT million square miles of the earth's surface lie between the lines of Capricorn and Cancer, within the tropics. Only about one fourth of this is land. The rest is sea. These general space proportions cannot be observed in writing a book about the tropics, however, because man is primarily a land animal, so that events on land are of much more immediate interest and concern to him than events in the sea.

Yet many groups of men have gone a long way toward developing amphibious habits. Much of the long process of human evolution surely took place in a forest setting; but surely also our ancestors early took to life on the open plains, and some of them to life along the seashore. Seashore man shows no signs of developing webbed feet or such-like physical adaptations to life in the water, but the sea has exerted a deep influence on the development of his cultural equipment; and the seafaring peoples in turn have repeatedly influenced the course of all human history.

Seashore-living and seafaring men, of course, are by no means peculiar to the tropics—witness the Eskimos, or the coastal Indians of British Columbia, or the Vikings. But no account of man in the tropics could leave the sea out, particularly because

212

the abundance of islands, peninsulas and archipelagos within the tropics means that the coast line available for human amphibious exploitation is immense.

The coastal tropical cultures have come to depend on the sea for food, for implements, for protection and for transportation. I am tempted to add "for recreation," but maybe recreation is a new idea, developed by Western civilization in the course of its struggles with the Intemperate climate and with the deadly monotony of some aspects of the industrialization process. Certainly Westerners seeking recreation in the West Indies or South Seas represent an intrusion on the tropical landscape (or seascape) rather than an indigenous element. And the local responses to this Western intrusion are better classed as "parasitic" than as "amphibious," even though they involve seaside hotels, beach concessions and fishing boats for hire.

For land animals generally the sea is a barrier; and only man, by building ships, has learned to use it as a highway. It was a limited highway for man until he acquired instrumental aids for navigation and the knowledge and resources for building large ships. Hence man's relations with the sea have been chiefly coastal; and our concern here will be with the coastal aspects of the sea, with what the biologists and the oceanographers call the "littoral zone."

The continuity of the seas and the peculiar properties of the salt water environment lead marine biologists and land biologists to approach their fields of study in quite different ways. Biologists on land are much concerned with geographical regions and climatic zones, but these things take a secondary place with students of the seas. These latter are apt first to think of the distinction between conditions near shore and conditions in the open sea, which they call, respectively, littoral and pelagic; or of the difference between bottom-dwelling organisms (which they call benthos) and free-swimming organisms (nekton) or free-floating organisms (plankton); or of conditions in the surface zone where light penetrates as distinguished from the abysmal zone of perpetual darkness and cold.

These kinds of distinctions override the differences between tropical and temperate zones, between summer and winter, between Eastern Hemisphere and Western Hemisphere, which seem so very important to the land-bound scientist. The term "tropical sea" does not, then, carry quite as many connotations of difference as does the term "tropical forest."

Yet, with this elaborate qualification, the term "tropical sea" is far from empty of meaning. Because the seas included within the area bounded by Capricorn and Cancer have many peculiarities, important not only to biologists, but to tropical man. To a surprising extent, these peculiarities hinge on the characteristics of a single group of organisms, the corals, which thus may well provide the chief focus of our attention here.

The corals are animals of the phylum coelenterata (which includes jelly-fish and sea anemones as well) that secrete a hard, lime skeleton. A great variety of marine animals have acquired the ability to make supporting or protecting structures out of lime (the shells of molluscs, for instance) and any animal that produces a coral-like skeleton might be called a "coral"—which would include quite a few rather different sorts of animals. Here, however, I want to discuss the "true corals" or "stony corals," the chief agencies in the building of coral reefs. These are a well-defined, related group of organisms which the zoologists call the Order Madreporaria of the Class Anthozoa of the Phylum Coelenterata.

The lump of coral that you find on the beach or in the curio shop represents the accumulated skeletons of innumerable individual polyps. Each of the tiny holes on the coral surface was originally the home of a single animal, on the average about pin-head size, which collected its food after the fashion of a sea anemone or a hydra, by catching microscopic organisms with its stinging tenacles.

There are about 2500 living species of true corals, each with its characteristic type of colony formation visible in the shape and structure of the calcareous skeleton. About five thousand other species of corals are known only as fossils, from the reefs of past ages.

The reef-building corals require warm, shallow waters. They flourish only when the water temperature is above 22° C. (71° F.), and they cannot stand prolonged exposure to temperatures below 18° C. (65° F.). They are thus pretty much limited to tropical and subtropical seas, where the water temperatures are generally above 70° F. They are scarce on the western coasts of South America and Africa because of the cold currents from the Antarctic that bathe those coasts, and they reach their greatest development in the Caribbean and Indo-Pacific regions. Reefs of fossil corals in the Arctic Seas and such like places are taken as another strong item of evidence that the climate of the earth did not always have its present glacial character: it is easier to imagine warm arctic seas than it is to imagine reef corals growing in icy waters.

The corals present endless problems for biological study. Apparently most of them feed at night, when the surface waters are rich in microscopic plankton (the plankton organisms migrate to lower depths during the daytime). The corals, however, cannot live without light, in part because they have developed a symbiotic arrangement with microscopic algae which, as plants, depend on light for photosynthesis. The single-celled algae which live in the coral body are thus busy all day building up starch from carbon dioxide produced by the respiration of the coral animals, while the corals are busy all night catching protozoa, copepods and so forth, and extracting the lime and other minerals from the sea water for building up the communal skeleton.

The reef-building corals grow only in shallow water, 150 feet being about the maximum depth at which they are found.

They are limited by the light, the temperature and perhaps other factors. They also require clear water, in constant motion; they are easily killed by mud or other sediments, and they depend on the moving water to wash such sediments away and to bring a constantly renewed food supply within reach. The growth of a coral reef thus occurs chiefly on the sea front, where the wave action meets these requirements.

Charles Darwin had an excellent chance to observe coral reefs during the voyage of the *Beagle,* and in 1842 he published a book called *The Structure and Distribution of Coral Reefs*—the starting point for a long series of books and articles by many different scientists on this problem. The problem of the origin of the reefs is still far from "solved," though the recent activities of army engineers working on coral reefs (such as Bikini) are providing an ever increasing fund of information. I cannot do more here than indicate the nature of the problem, though the importance of corals in the economy of the tropics requires that reef formation be given some attention.

There are three kinds of coral reefs: fringing reefs, barrier reefs and atolls. A fringing reef occurs directly along the shore line, extending out for a few feet or for as much as a quarter of a mile; it consists of the actively growing reef edge, or front, and a slightly lower reef flat extending back to the shore, mostly covered with coral sand and mud with other debris, inhabited by organisms (including some coral colonies) that can stand tidal exposure.

A barrier reef is similar to a fringing reef, except that it is separated from the shore line by a lagoon that may be 300 feet or so deep, and 10 miles or so wide. The most famous of these reefs is the Great Barrier Reef of Australia, which is some 1200 miles long and at places as much as 90 miles off shore, extending from Cape York to end almost precisely at the Tropic of Capricorn. This reef has long fascinated zoologists, oceanographers, geographers and tourists, and has been described in many books, among which a recent one by T. C. Roughley is notable because of its beautiful color photographs.

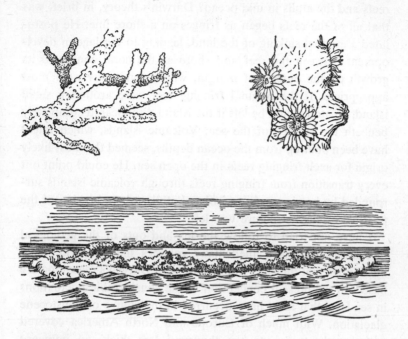

A Coral Atoll (copy of the drawing used by Darwin in the *Voyage of the Beagle*). The drawings show branching growth form and detail of coral animals.

An atoll is a more or less circular or horseshoe-shaped reef enclosing a lagoon in the open sea—sometimes only a mile or so across, sometimes 40 or 50 miles across. Atoll formations are characteristic of the South Pacific. Familiar enough from the writings of the South Sea romancers, they became even more familiar in the course of the naval operations of World War II, when the Coral Sea became part of everyone's vocabulary, and a matter of firsthand experience to countless G.I.s.

The fringing reefs seem understandable enough, given the nature of coral growth; but how can we account for the barrier reefs and the atolls in mid ocean? Darwin's theory, in brief, was that all of the reefs began as fringes on a shore line. He postulated a gradual sinking of the land, leading to the lagoon development between the reef and shore as the coral continued its growth on the outer reef margin, where conditions were most appropriate. If the original fringing reef were around a small island, an atoll would be left if the island disappeared completely beneath the surface of the sea. Volcanic islands, which might have been built up from the ocean depths, seemed the most likely origin for such fringing reefs in the open sea. He could point out every transition from fringing reefs through volcanic islands surrounded by barrier reefs, to isolated atolls, where no sign of the possible original structure was left.

I have not tried to follow the ins and outs of the geological discussions that have filled many volumes since Darwin's day, but I judge that the chief modifications of Darwin's reasoning are based on the present conception of the considerable fluctuations in sea level that must have occurred in the course of Pleistocene glaciation. With much of Europe and North America covered with ice sheets five to ten thousand feet thick, an immense amount of water would have been locked up, causing an appreciable lowering of sea level. Estimates of the amount of variation in sea level differ considerably, but a conservative guess would be that the seas, at the maximum of glaciation, would have been at least 150 feet lower than now. The gradual rise in sea level with the melting of the ice (which is still going on) would provide favorable conditions for the formation of the barrier and atoll types of reef.

The rate of growth of corals is not as well known as it should be, since the reefs occur in the tropics and scientists mostly stay near universities in the north; but various measurements indicate that slow-growing, massive corals may increase only 5 mm. (a quarter inch) a year, while some of the branching kinds may grow almost a foot a year. One author guesses that a reef 150 feet thick could be formed in something between 1000 and 8000 years. The corals at least could easily keep pace with any rise in the ocean due to melting glacier ice.

A tourist on almost any tropical coast nowadays can take a ride in a glass-bottomed boat and thus get a glimpse of the colorful life that is associated with a coral reef. It is one "tour" that is well worth taking, though an even clearer idea of the variety of life and the complexity of its interrelations can be obtained (with no danger of seasickness) by a visit to the magnificent exhibits of the American Museum of Natural History in New York.

The transparency of the water of tropical lagoons and bays is amazing, and I have been looking through various books to see whether I could find an explanation—without much success. The transparency of sea water depends on the amount of suspended matter that it contains and to a lesser extent on the angle of the light rays. Since the light in the tropics is more generally directly overhead, penetration would be greater than in higher latitudes. The clearest water, seen from above, is deep blue, and in one series of measurements with a white disc, the disc was visible to a depth of 200 feet in the deep blue water of the tropical Sargasso Sea; but it was visible to 150 feet in the blue water between Antarctic pack-ice.

The transparency of tropical lagoons must be due chiefly to the small amount of suspended matter. Perhaps this is related to the efficiency of the corals and other animals in constantly removing debris and in keeping the bottom covered with hard coral rocks or sand. In the Caribbean, at least, I would think the weak tides, which do not set up the strong currents of higher latitudes, would also help account for the clearness. In river estuaries and around mangrove swamps tropical waters can be muddy enough.

There is plenty to see in these transparent waters of the coral reefs. Any very deep appreciation, with the reef as with the forest, requires prolonged observation and careful study; but there is enough reward for even the most superficial glance. The most striking things about the reef habitat, I should say, are the colors and the details of form. This contrasts markedly with the tropical forest habitat which, as I have tried to emphasize, is not colorful, and in which the overwhelming impression depends on the architectural structure, not on detail: on the great buttressed trunks, on the endless variations in the limited forest vistas, on the still dampness of the atmosphere, on the dim light that filters through the remote canopy.

The general association of "colorfulness" with the tropics may be misleading, but there is no denying the variety and brilliance of color in the reef habitat. The difference between variety of color on land and in the sea stems from the fact that the whole economy of land organisms is based on seed plants, which are green; while the economy of the sea is based on algae, which are many-colored. The algae and the seed plants both depend on a green pigment, chlorophyl, for carrying out their basic industry of photosynthesis, of building up starch from the carbon dioxide free in the air or dissolved in water; but with the seed plants, the color of the conspicuous synthesizing organs—the leaves—depends directly on the chlorophyl, while with the algae the green of the chlorophyl is very generally masked by accessory pigments of different colors.

Much, too, depends on the fact that most of the photosynthesis of the sea is carried out by microscopic organisms, by algae floating free in the surface layers of the water. Thus we do not see the individual organisms on which the whole economy of the sea depends, while we do see the seed plants on which all of the other land organisms depend.

With a coral reef, then, the whole physical structure can depend on animals growing in fixed positions—on the corals—

while the chemical structure depends on floating plants, too small to be seen as individuals. The live coral colonies themselves show a great variety of colors: purples, reds, greens, browns; and the algae and anemones that grow with them show an equal variety. The fixed animals thus provide a colorful background into which the active animals must fit. The fish, shrimp and crabs that show "protective coloration" must necessarily be as gaudy as the background against which they seek protection. The fishes that do not show protective semblance seem to be gaudy out of sheer exuberance—or perhaps as a result of sexual selection or something of that sort.

There is endless material for study among these organisms of a reef: their complicated methods of reproduction and growth, their relations with each other and with the physical environment in which they live. These relationships, however, involve general biological principles rather than any special characteristics of the tropics, so that they are not directly related to the subject of this book. Some remarks about oceanic geography, however, may be germane.

Since the seas are continuous around the surface of the globe, their subdivision into geographical units is more difficult than in the case of the discontinuous continents. Oceanographers generally recognize three oceans—the Pacific, the Atlantic and the Indian. The "Arctic Ocean" is more properly a sea, comparable to the Mediterranean or the Caribbean. The seas around the Antarctic continent are sometimes called the "Antarctic Ocean," but the limits of such an "ocean" would be hard to define.

Organisms of the open seas encounter no barriers in going from one ocean to another, especially if they can tolerate the not too low temperatures of the southern hemisphere. Geography is meaningless, then, for such organisms. The organisms of the shore and of shallow water, however, are bound to the continental geography, especially since they are apt to have rather narrow temperature requirements.

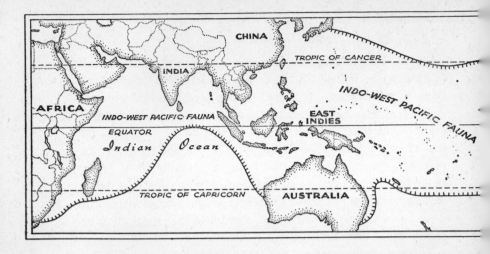

Four barriers to coastal organisms stretch across the tropics: the land barrier of the American continents, the ocean barrier of the mid-Atlantic, the African land barrier, and the empty oceanic spaces of the east Pacific. Four biotic regions are defined by these barriers: the Atlantic Tropical American fauna, which includes the Gulf of Mexico, the Caribbean and the east coast of South America; the West African fauna; the Indo-West Pacific fauna, which includes the shores of the Indian Ocean, the East Indies, Northern Australia and the islands of the South Seas; and the Pacific Tropical American fauna.

The Indo-West Pacific is by far the largest of these regions, extending from the east African coast to the Hawaiian Islands. It is in this region that the coral reefs, with all of their hangers-on, reach their maximum development; and here, with the Polynesians, we find the most truly amphibious of human cultures. The Atlantic Tropical American region is similar, though developed on a much smaller scale. The native cultures of the Caribbean must have been almost as amphibious as the Polynesian cultures, but the Caribbean cultures were very quickly and very thoroughly erased by the cultural explosion that was triggered by Columbus.

The West African region and the Pacific Tropical American

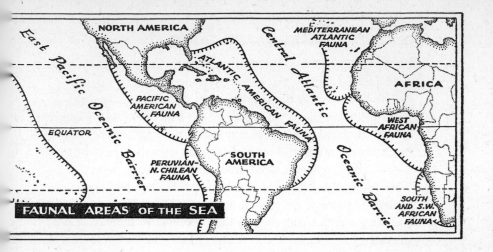

Map labels: NORTH AMERICA, East Pacific, PACIFIC AMERICAN FAUNA, EQUATOR, Oceanic Barrier, PERUVIAN-N.CHILEAN FAUNA, FAUNAL AREAS OF THE SEA, Central Atlantic, ATLANTIC AMERICAN FAUNA, SOUTH AMERICA, MEDITERRANEAN ATLANTIC FAUNA, AFRICA, WEST AFRICAN FAUNA, Oceanic Barrier, SOUTH AND S.W. AFRICAN FAUNA

region have few islands, which greatly reduces the possibility of the development of a rich littoral biota, or of a truly amphibious human culture. They are also exposed to cold currents—the Peru current (Humboldt's current) in America and the Benguela current in Africa—which results in lower than average tropical water temperatures, so that the growth of corals, for instance, is circumscribed.

This matter of ocean currents is interesting, and surely important in any description of the tropical environment; but the general subject is too complex for synopsis here. The most spectacular and the best studied current is the Gulf Stream system which flows along the east coast of North America. The first part of this, the "Florida current," flows out of the Gulf of Mexico and along the Florida coast with considerable velocity— a maximum speed of something like four miles per hour—carrying warm tropical water across the mid-Atlantic to the shores of Europe.

The mechanics of these ocean currents are not well understood but it seems probable that the initial velocity of the Gulf Stream is due to the "head" of water in the Gulf of Mexico. The trade winds and resulting westerly surface ocean drifts in the equatorial region pile up water in the Gulf of Mexico. Sea level on the Gulf of Mexico side of Florida, because of this, is 19 cm, (7½ inches) higher than on the Atlantic side.

The backwash of the Florida current creates a huge, slowly-moving eddy between the coast and the Bermuda Islands known as the "Sargasso Sea." This is north of the band of the tropics, but it represents a spill-over of tropical organisms and tropical water. The Sargassum weed grows in the coastal waters of the West Indies. Broken parts of the plants, buoyed by a system of bladder-like floats, are carried northward by the Florida current and caught in this eddy, where they continue to grow for a considerable time, forming the floating mats familiar to everyone who has spent much time leaning over a steamer rail in Caribbean waters.

The idea that ships could get caught in these floating masses of weed is pure myth; but they are spectacular enough to always catch the eye of the traveler. They are interesting to the naturalist, too, because a whole special fauna of fish, shrimps, snails and worms makes its home in the weed—shore animals that have worked out adaptations to this special form of "pelagic" existence in the open sea.

Since this is a book on the tropics, it is perfectly natural that I should put more emphasis on what the tropics has than on what it lacks; if I bring out any advantages of the north, it is reluctantly and incidentally. But in this present discussion of the oceans I cannot see any way of avoiding mention of the fact that the major fishing regions of the earth are all outside of the tropics. These major regions, where fishing is a basic industry, are the American northeast (Grand Banks and so forth), the Pacific northwest, the European north Atlantic, and the Asiatic coast, especially around the Japanese archipelago.

How does it happen that the tropics have not got the world's richest fishing grounds, in view of my general thesis of the abundance of tropical life? I should like to pass this off as an example of the haywire development of Western industrial culture, alleging that the large scale exploitation of fishing resources was a consequence of the industrialization process, limited by transportation problems to the vicinity of concentrations of

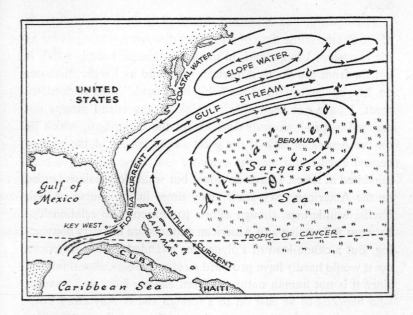

industrial peoples. This has something to do with it, I think; but it also appears that there are really more fish in these northern waters than in the tropics. This is related to the greater abundance of plankton, of microscopic food, in northern waters, which in turn has some explanation in the nitrogen cycle of the ocean. There are more different kinds of fish in the tropics, but no one kind compares in abundance with the teeming cod of northern waters.

Seafaring is no more a peculiar tropical characteristic than fishing. As a matter of fact, seafaring and fishing go pretty much hand-in-hand: witness, for instance, the exploits of the Scandinavian and Mediterranean peoples. There is, however, one great area of seafaring and fishing peoples within the tropics that warrants some special attention: the Indo-West Pacific region, and especially the Melanesian and Polynesian cultures of the South Seas.

These people had colonized almost all of the habitable islands of the Pacific at the time of European discovery, getting as far as the Hawaiian Islands and, in the south, Easter Island, which is not far from the South American mainland as Pacific distances go. Maybe "almost all of the habitable islands" is an understatement. I have not been able to think of any island groups not reached in pre-European days except the Galapagos, which lie on the American side of the great empty spaces of the eastern central Pacific and there is evidence that these may have been inhabited at times. I have no doubt but what Polynesians landed on the American coast itself many times in the course of their Pacific wanderings, though efforts to demonstrate relationships between Polynesian and American cultures are not very convincing. But a canoe-load of Polynesians stranded on the American coast would hardly have provided a recognizable cultural impact, since it is not human nature to learn eagerly from any stranger who happens to be cast on to a foreign shore. Any stray Polynesians were most likely trussed up and promptly sacrificed to some appropriate god.

It is said that vessels from the Society Islands made voyages to the very limits of Polynesia, to Hawaii in the north and to New Zealand in the south. The larger, ocean-going vessels were more than a hundred feet long and could if necessary carry several hundred people with water and provisions such as pigs and chickens. The Polynesians had no instrumental aids to navigation, but their navigators knew the winds, seas, sky and stars intimately, and were amazingly skilled at holding to a course. Although they must, to be sure, often have missed their way, dying in the open sea or landing in some unexpected place.

Both the Polynesians and the Melanesians have a certain

amount of agriculture, cultivating yams and taro, collecting coconuts and breadfruit, and raising pigs and chickens. But they also depend to a large extent on the sea for food, and on some of the coral islands where "soil" hardly occurs, agriculture is limited and the people are almost completely dependent on the sea. The fish are caught on shell hooks of various designs, with nets and traps of various sorts, or speared, or shot with bow and arrow, or poisoned in tidal pools with appropriate plant juices. Fishing may become involved with elaborate ritual, as in the case of bonito fishing in the Solomons. These fish turn up along the coast in small shoals in March, to remain for a few weeks, and many important ceremonies center on this short fishing season, including the initiation of the young men into adult status in the community.

Even more spectacular, as a sea-calendar event, is the appearance of the palolo worms, which swarm at the surface of the sea with precise regularity one night a year when they are caught in great numbers to be dried and smoked, furnishing a staple "relish" of the food supply for the rest of the year.

But in discussing fishing, we are treating one item in the long catalogue of the resources available to man in the tropics for the development of his cultures and civilizations. The fisheries seem to be a rather poor tropical resource. I cannot help but feel that this is partly a result of our failure to apply the methods of scientific and technological study to the problems of tropical marine resources, and that in the long run the tropical seas may turn out to be a rich source of food and other supplies for man's developing needs. For the present, however, the tropical seas as a resource are dwarfed by the possibilities of the tropical lands, which I want to discuss in the next chapter.

CHAPTER XIV

★

The Resources of the Tropics

THE use of a word like "resources" indicates that we have entered the realm of economics, which by one dictionary definition is "the science that investigates . . . the material means of satisfying human desires." We are looking at the world from the point of view of its utility to man—as a storehouse of materials to be exploited, conserved, hoarded or wasted, or as a garden plot that may be cultivated or neglected in a variety of ways.

The resources of the world for a cabbage butterfly can be studied in terms of the availability of cabbages; for an owl, in terms of field mice and nesting sites. The economy of food-gathering man was probably not much more complicated, being rather like that of any omnivorous mammal—a raccoon, for instance. But with the acquisition and development of culture, all of this changed and the economy of man started gaining complexity, at first slowly but later, with the specialization and diversification of civilization, at a dizzily increasing rate. Today's result often seems to be an economy that is beyond the comprehension of any of its human creators; or at least, quite plainly beyond my comprehension.

I wish I had the knowledge to give a general survey of the economy of man in the tropics. Such a survey is greatly needed

228

in view of the present Western concern over the parts of the world that it arrogantly classes as "backward" (which would include the whole wide belt of the tropics) and because of the delicate problems of relationship between the tropical producers of raw materials and the northern consumers and processors of those materials. The wealth of the contemporary world has accrued to the benefit of the processors of raw materials rather than of the producers of raw materials, and this has led the producers (which includes the tropical peoples) to want to share in the processing, to "industrialize" themselves—a change that is well under way in countries like India and Brazil.

To make a proper survey of the economy of tropical man, we should have to review the modern history of international trade and its companion, international politics. Trade, as I pointed out in the beginning of this book, seems to have been the direct stimulus for the geographical expansion of the West in the 15th and 16th centuries, and it has continued to dominate the relationships between the West and tropical peoples. At first, the list of things that the West wanted from the tropics was paltry indeed—chiefly spices, and a few luxury articles like precious woods and jewels. The Spaniards were looking for spices when they stumbled into America, though when they discovered that they could loot the local peoples of their accumulated gold, they forgot all about other materials until the ready supply of gold had been exhausted.

The list of tropical products useful to the West grew rapidly, as the West discovered what the tropics had to offer, and as the complexities of its own technologies made ever more diversified demands. But this trade relationship from the beginning was a lopsided affair, because the West found that its armaments and technical skill enabled it to back its tropical trading with force. There has never been much open bartering, much free exchange of goods or services between the peoples of Europe and the peoples of the tropics, because while Europe has held out one hand open to receive the goods that the tropics had to offer, the other hand has held, not fair exchange, but a loaded pistol. The West has exploited the tropics, but after a fashion that has made "exploitation" sound more like robbery than like trade or development.

Partly this was because the West wanted much, but had little to offer in return. This is very striking in the accounts of the first European voyages. The Portuguese, coming upon the luxury and wealth of India, could offer nothing for the jewels, silks and spices that they coveted except glass beads, tinkling bells and bales of cotton cloth. This sufficed sometimes as trade for gold with the people of simple cultures; but it could not be made a basis for trade with the sophisticated cultures until gunpowder and murder had weighted the scales.

The West, of course, soon found more useful trade goods than glass beads and tinkling bells, and in the long run it has exchanged machines and manufactured goods—the product of skilled labor—for tropical raw materials—the product of unskilled labor. But this still does not represent much of a balance, especially from the point of view of building up standards of living among the unskilled laborers of the tropics comparable with those of the skilled laborers of the West. And the tropical peoples have come to want a share in the rewards of skilled labor —hence their desire for an industrial economy.

No tropical region has as yet succeeded in developing an industrial economy, and all sorts of explanations have been adduced for this. I suspect that the explanation does not lie in lack of capital, lack of power sources, lack of raw materials, or lack of potential skill in the labor force, so much as it lies in the cultural orientation of the tropical peoples themselves. And the reorientation of the cultural pattern (which would include political and social systems) will be no simple task, either for outsiders or for local governing groups. We know that it can be done, because we have an example in Japan: a non-Western nation that deliberately and successfully adopted the Western industrial system.

The case of Japan, I think, should be carefully studied by the Western missionaries of industrialization, and by local peoples who want to industrialize themselves. The change seems to have taken place with relatively little importation of either capital or experts: which makes me doubt whether the prime need, in the case of other non-industrial countries, is for shipments of Western capital and Western experts. The Japanese transformation perhaps depended most on a tight, autocratic control of the economy by a group of people who were determined to carry through with the industrialization process, and who were able to dictate and control the required measures. This is hardly in accord with the principles of democracy, and presents, I think, a real dilemma to those Westerners who want to remake the world in accord with both democratic and industrial ideas at the same time.

I do not believe that the industrialization of Japan depended on its "stimulating" climate, which I suppose would be the argument of geographers like Ellsworth Huntington. Nor do I believe that it depended on any superior intellectual ability of the Japanese people. The intellectual ability of the peoples of Japan in the north and of Java in the south would seem quite comparable in the days before Western contact. And the fact that Japan built itself into an industrial power while Java remained a producer of raw materials seems hardly explicable on the grounds of difference in racial intelligence or difference in climate. The difference, it seems to me, is most easily explained by differences in the modern political history of the two countries, especially the nature of their Western contacts, and perhaps by more subtle differences in their cultural orientation— though these latter would be difficult to analyze.

Tropical peoples are not interested in industrialization because they think it would look pretty to have factories scattered over their landscapes, or even because of an overwhelming desire to have their automobiles marked "made in Java." What they want, as I said, is the standard of living that they associate with industrialization. They want, as individuals, the comforts and luxuries of individual Westerners; and they want, as nations, the power and independence of the Western nations. They may find that this is a mess of potage, but they understandably want to see for themselves. And also, in many cases, they see no way of supporting their multiplying populations except through industrialization, quite regardless of the average of living standards among the members of those populations.

With standards of living and with population pressures, I have got well outside of the range of topics that I planned to deal with in this book. Both, however, must obviously be given serious attention by anyone interested in the development of the tropics or in the fostering of better understanding among the peoples of this planet. Both also are intimately related to the problems of the utilization of natural resources. What use is to be made of the resources: are they to be developed to permit the mere survival of a maximum possible number of people, or is the sheer weight of numbers to be subordinated to attempts at increasing the comfort and happiness of people in general?

This is where economics becomes entangled with ethics, since the one is concerned with means, the other with ends. I do not see how any separation of the two is possible, because surely means must always be evaluated in terms of the ends to be attained; and ends can hardly be weighed without consideration of the possible means of attainment.

Before getting back to more solid, factual grounds, I would like to insert a few comments on this matter of standards of living. It seems to me that the subject has been too exclusively a preoccupation of economists, and that it has been dealt with almost entirely in Western terms. This is natural, because economics as a science has developed along with the industrial,

Western civilization, and is dedicated to the explanation of the workings of that civilization. Some of the generalizations derived from such study probably have universal application, but this, I think, must be proved by testing under widely varying conditions; yet such testing outside of the Western economic system is rarely undertaken.

Standard of living, for instance, is most often handled in terms of money income, in relation to the purchasing power of such income. The propriety of this might be questioned even within the context of Western civilization, though it certainly is a convenient measure for comparisons between, say, Sweden and England, or Connecticut and Alabama, or steel workers and lawyers. But I doubt whether per capita income in Sumatra has any meaning in relation to per capita income in England—though I often see such comparisons made.

This matter of standards of living and their meaning would certainly be a fruitful subject for cooperative investigation by diverse sorts of people, such as economists, anthropologists and geographers. Kinds of satisfactions would have to be studied, so that an automobile in the West could be balanced against an outrigger canoe in Polynesia. Also some means should be found of evaluating the difference in sheer difficulty of living in different geographical environments. In the north, an impressive amount of energy—which means money—must go into housing, heating and clothing, if physical misery is to be alleviated; while in the tropics the same end may be attained without any comparable expenditure. Food and food costs must similarly be studied within the different cultural and climatic contexts.

The study of population pressures, on analysis, also turns out to be a very complex affair. This is probably why there is so little agreement among the various people who have studied the matter. We have on the one hand the disciples of the dismal theorem of Malthus (that population tends always to grow to the limit of the food supply and to be checked by misery, disease and famine); and on the other hand the optimistic converts to the limitless possibilities of modern technology, who maintain that with proper utilization of solar energy, men can be packed on to the planetary surface to the extent of standing room only. The excess after that, I suppose, will be shot off to new worlds on rockets.

Any time that I start to think about population problems, I get entangled with this same question of satisfactions that so complicates the problem of standards of living. In some cases it is easy. The coal miner in West Virginia or the coolie in China is clearly leading a hazardous, unsatisfactory existence, by almost any standard, and something should be done about it. But I am not at all sure about the value of changing the coolie into a miner, or the nomad into a factory hand, or in short, about the propriety of trying to shift any one cultural pattern into some other cultural pattern. And least of all am I sure that salvation lies in imposing the Western pattern on the whole world; though perhaps now the greatest danger lies in the Russian pattern, since this seems to be the most virulently missionary of all.

But I intended to write about resources in this chapter, not about systems of populations or standards of living, though these various subjects are so inextricably united as to make separate discussion difficult. The glue that holds them all together, of course, is culture pattern. To say that resources are culture-bound seems at first glance odd, because we are completely used to thinking about materials in Western terms; yet it is obvious enough that the resources of the Congo region, for instance, are quite different for the forest pygmies, for the agricultural Bantu, and for the intruding Europeans. Our interest in tropic resources here, however, is largely from the point of view of Western civilization, especially in relation to the global economy of modern times.

We customarily divide resources into "renewable" and "non-renewable": into those which are geared to the continuing processes of nature, and those which man mines from the accumulated surplus of past geological ages. These latter are a cause of constant concern to students of our economy, because surely within some measurable future we shall have used up the accumulation of easily available oil, coal, iron, gold and so forth. The fatal limit has so far always receded as new supplies and new reserves have been discovered; but man goes on spending at a reckless rate, and no one has suggested that the reserves of all of these specific materials will turn out to be infinite.

These fixed resources inherited from the geological past show no clear relation to the present climatic zoning of our planet, and almost all of them are found at one place or another within the tropics. There are no great supplies of coal in close relation to supplies of iron ore, and this may be one of the reasons for the industrial backwardness of the tropics, since heavy industry has so far depended on bringing iron ore and coal into easy juxtaposition. But there are large reserves of iron in places like Brazil, Venezuela, India and various parts of Africa which will probably be utilized in ever increasing degree.

There are coal deposits in many parts of the tropics, but they are limited in comparison with the coal deposits of the North Temperate zone. I do not recall reading any explanation of this, but it may well be the result of climate zonation in the coal-forming periods of the past. Perhaps bacterial action was too rapid in the tropics to permit peat-like accumulations. Present-day peat is pretty much limited to high latitudes (though there are things like the Florida Everglades) and even humus or leaf mold does not accumulate in a tropical forest. On the other hand, coal beds are generally assumed to have been formed in a mild climate, and our reconstructed picture of the Carboniferous coal-forming forests would find its nearest counterpart in present tropical swamps.

Oil is abundant enough in the tropics, with great fields in Venezuela, Peru, Arabia and the East Indies. The oil, of course, is largely used by the United States and Europe, which results in an unbalanced economy for the oil-producing country. Venezuela is the type case of this, since the whole life of the country has come to depend on the oil exports. Even the oil companies worry about the effect of this, but the various efforts to develop a more diversified economy seem not to have been very effective. Perhaps the only solution is to wait until the oil supplies begin to run out, when circumstances will force the development of other resources.

The tropics have their fair share of the various metals. Tin, now chiefly mined in Bolivia and Malaya, is almost a tropical monopoly. There also seem to be greater reserves of bauxite, the commonest source of aluminum, in the tropics than elsewhere; there are large deposits on all of the continents, and it is the chief export of Dutch Guiana. Gold, silver, copper, lead, zinc and such like metals are found in many places. Radium production was long a monopoly of the Belgian Congo; and the Congo gains added importance now as a source of uranium. A good fraction of the world's supply of many of the rare metals like vanadium, tungsten, titanium and beryllium, comes from the tropics.

The possibilities of hydroelectric developments in the tropics have hardly begun to be realized; and these may, in the long run, be the chief source of power. But the various mineral and power resources, impressive enough in the listing, are widely scattered, and it seems unlikely that any particular tropical region has the industrial possibilities of, say, the Midlands of England, the Ruhr region of Central Europe, or the northeastern United States.

But this, it seems to me, need hardly be treated as a handicap. The characteristic resources of the tropics are not of this exploitative, time-limited sort; they lie rather in the dynamic, renewable processes of nature that will maintain human economy long after the Midlands and the Ruhr have been exhausted. The resources of the tropics should be calculated in terms of sunshine and warmth and (in the equatorial region, at least) rainfall: which combine to produce the most favorable conditions possible for vegetation. This, for man as for all other animals, is the basic resource.

Plant products are, of course, the chief resource of the tropics now: not only for home consumption, but for export. I have found export figures for 44 different tropical countries; in only 9 cases was the chief export a mineral, and in only one case (Madagascar) was it meat or meat products. Of the remaining 34 countries, the chief export was coffee in 8 cases, cotton (5), sugar (5), rubber (4), rice (3), tobacco (2), bananas (2), peanuts (2), jute (1, India), copra (1, the Philippines) and tea (1, Ceylon). The copra list would be greatly extended if figures were available for the South Sea Island groups.

It always amazes me that coffee, which seems such a trivial item of human consumption, should occupy such an important place in international trade. It is the major export of one large country (Brazil) and of seven smaller ones (Guatemala, El Salvador, Costa Rica, Colombia, Haiti, Ethiopia, and the Portuguese colony of Angola).

The list of the chief exports of the various tropical countries gives a rather poor idea of the nature and diversity of the plant products that the tropics contribute to the pool of human resources, because many items that are of great importance in our economy occupy secondary places in the trade lists based on dollar value or tonnage. Spices, for instance, do not appear on this list, though they were the prime objective of the first European penetration of the tropics, and though we still depend on the tropics for our supplies of pepper, cinnamon, nutmeg and cloves. Nor do the fine woods, like mahogany, ebony and teak, appear in the list. Nor things like chicle, the basis of our chewing gum, which comes from the sap of a forest tree that grows in southern Mexico, British Honduras and Guatemala.

The list of actual tropical plant products, however, is of less interest than the question of tropical potentialities. Much of the discussion about man's future on this planet turns on the question of the possibilities of tropical agriculture. There is a remarkable scarcity of information on which to base any conclusions, but this has by no means hampered discussion. It has, in fact, made extensive and contradictory discussion possible, leading to very positive—and completely conflicting—conclusions, supported by a varied assortment of opinions and prejudices.

My own feeling is that man will come to depend more and more upon the tropics, because within the tropics lies his greatest pool of unrealized, renewable resources. This does not mean that I believe the tropics can support infinitely multiplying numbers of people, or that such use of its resources would be desirable even if possible. Nor does it mean that I think we now know how to develop and manage the resources of the tropics. But I think we could learn; and furthermore, that we shall have to learn, if we are to continue making progress toward our avowed goal of finding more satisfactory ways of life for mankind as a whole.

There are many obstacles to the full utilization of tropical resources, and when I go over a catalogue of these obstacles in my mind, I am not at all sure about the probability of our success in overcoming them. But then, it has always been easy to take a gloomy view of the future; and the antidote for gloom seems not to be so much any reasoned calculation, as a sort of faith in man's ability to "muddle through."

An important set of obstacles lies not in the tropics, but in the nature of Western civilization. Some students, like William Vogt and Fairfield Osborn, argue plausibly that the West itself has gained its present prosperity and power by living recklessly on capital, by "plundering" the planet. The West, in this view, has not only mined and wasted its fossil fuels and minerals, but, in a quite comparable way, has wasted resources that should be renewable—its soils, its forests, its sources of water. If the West cannot find a means of adjusting its own economy to the processes of nature in the Western environment, it is hardly in any position to help other peoples make such adjustments in other environments.

For present purposes, however, we are not so much concerned with the internal problems of Western civilization, as with its relation to the tropics. In this, I am always bothered by the Western arrogance, by its assurance that it knows all of the answers and can quite readily fix everything so that the tropical peoples can live happily ever after, if they will only listen. This philosophy underlies all of the various programs of international technical assistance that are so popular these days, and especially the programs of the United States which are aimed at the uplift of practically everybody else.

I suppose I have been a part of this American missionary movement myself for most of my life, so that it would be ungrateful of me to start throwing stones at it now. But I have taken comfort from the fact that I belonged to the rather small and subsidiary wing of the missionary movement that was trying to learn about things, instead of trying to change things: though I and my fellows have always been conscious that the things that we learned would, sometime, by someone, be used as a basis for action.

I have also, however, had a chance to watch the active missionaries, the reforming missionaries, and this has led to my increasing doubt about the present ability of Western technicians to solve the problems of the tropics. There is no denying the technical achievements of the West, in medicine, in agriculture, in industry, in education; and no denying that the West, in science, has discovered a powerful tool for manipulating nature to achieve definite human satisfactions. But these sciences and technologies have all developed within the Western context, and we are often quite blind to the adaptations that may be necessary if they are to be exported to other cultures and other climates.

This digression is meant to be background for some remarks

about how much we need to learn about tropical agriculture, about the management of the renewable resources of the tropics, before we shall be able to give much helpful advice to our southern neighbors. This need for more knowledge about agriculture seems to me particularly striking because agricultural practices are intimately linked with climate, and it is in climate, in the basic nature of the conditions of plant growth, that the tropics differ most from the north. I do not see how one can learn, in New York or Illinois or Kansas, to deal with the tropical environment; yet we quite confidently send our young experts from such places to Colombia and Siam to tell the "natives" what they ought to do.

The alternative, to try to help the development of scientific and technical institutions within the tropics, will be slow and far from easy. Science—its methods and attitudes—seems never to have taken root in any tropical culture; yet such an establishment will surely be the necessary preliminary to the development of scientific control over local conditions. I do not understand this failure of science to show indigenous development within the tropics, though I have spent a great deal of time thinking about the matter. The reasons are probably both complex and obscure, and their understanding will probably, in part at least, depend on the understanding of the converse situation, of the causes of the great contemporary development of science in Western culture—which are far from clear.

I have argued in this book that man, as an animal, is a product of evolution in the tropical environment; and that much of human cultural evolution took place in the tropics, including the first steps toward agriculture, and perhaps the beginnings of the complex cultures that we call "civilizations." But I cannot make out a case for the tropical origins of science, despite the fact that some of its basic tools, like the system of numbers, came from India. Science as we know it is a characteristic product of modern Western Europe, which has been extended to North

America along with the rest of Western culture, and which has been successfully adopted by two other civilizations, the Russian (or "Orthodox" of Toynbee's scheme) and the Japanese.

I sometimes suspect that the Russian and Japanese adoptions of science are hothouse affairs, dependent on the artificial stimulation of governments anxious to get the material fruits of scientific growth; though I have to admit that this hothouse cultivation seems to be successful enough, at least for a while. But generally, in the West, science seems to have grown in spite of government, and the aims of science are often in conflict with the aims of government, which are apt to be concerned with national interests, and dedicated to secrecy and the suppression of ideas and actions that conflict with immediate national self-interest. Science in the West has depended not so much upon government, as upon its own organizations in the form of societies, academies and universities, and upon the support of occasional farseeing individuals—sometimes princes and ministers, and sometimes private citizens.

But this is getting rather far afield from the subject of tropical resources; and I have become very unscientific by sketching in a few vague and broad ideas when there is no chance to fill in the supporting evidence, or to make the inevitable qualifications and to cite the real and apparent contradictions. My point is that the scientific method, which appears to me as a product of a total cultural situation, needs to be applied if tropical potentialities are to be realized; and that the development of this scientific method requires something more than governmental edict or manipulation of foreign policy. Unfortunately, I cannot be very specific about this "something more," because such ideas as I have about the requirements for the scientific development of the tropics are far from specific.

It will be interesting to see what happens in Indonesia. I have never heard anyone deny the intelligence of the Javanese; and they have had in their midst for a long time a transplant of science brought by the Dutch, who developed first class laboratories and experiment stations. The trouble is that Dutch science, like Dutch government, was imposed; and the baby may get dumped out with the bath water in the course of present clean-up operations.

India will be another interesting country to watch, since India has produced undeniably great men in mathematics and physics, and perfectly competent men in all branches of science. Will it be possible to direct this intelligence toward the solution of local problems of economy and resources?

In Latin America, I have always felt that one of the prime problems was to break down national barriers, so that a scientific community could develop with the whole of both of the American continents for its field of action—so that chemists and biologists and their ideas could move as freely from Colombia to Peru to Guatemala as from Michigan to Massachusetts. There are beginnings of such developments in places like the Inter-American School of Agriculture in Costa Rica; and in such institutions, I think, lies the hope of the future.

When science has achieved this adaptation and development in the tropics, we shall begin to collect the necessary information on which to gauge the possibilities of tropical resources, and with which to plan their management. We shall have facts about crops and soils and industrial processes instead of wishful thinking and prejudiced pessimism.

My own hope for the future of tropical resources lies in exploiting the possibilities that must be latent in the environment that creates the tropical rain forest. I have already dwelt on the nature of this forest environment at some length; yet, as I have pointed out, man has not yet found any satisfactory way of mastering this immense potential of vegetable growth. He can only hack away at the margins of the great forest, cutting it down and burning it to get rid of it, so that he can plant a crop or two of insignificant corn, or by constant vigilance maintain pastures which get converted into food and leather inefficiently by way of a few cattle. Man has, by this slow process, achieved very considerable inroads on the forest area, attaining a cumulative destruction that justly alarms the conservationists. But he has not learned to work with the climatic forces that create the forest; he opposes them by trying to convert the forest growth into peanut fields or cotton fields or corn patches. And when this conversion fails, he deplores the poverty of tropical soils, and derides the possibility of agricultural development where "the downpours leach out minerals from the upper levels and the equatorial sun rapidly burns out organic matter" (quoting from William Vogt).

How can the soils be "poor" that support the most complex vegetative growth known on the planet? It seems to me that it is simply that we haven't learned how to work with the environment; that we try to apply, in the Congo or Amazon, methods that work well enough on our Midwestern prairies, and that when we fail, we blame the soil and the climate instead of the method of agriculture.

Some of the more successful tropical crops—coffee and rubber, for instance—represent a partial utilization of the forest situation, but these only scratch the surface of the possibilities. I recently read Egon Glesinger's persuasive book, *The Coming Age of Wood,* and this seems to me to give a glimpse at the probable role of forestry in man's economic future. Glesinger is preoccupied with the possibilities of northern forests, because research in places like Germany, Sweden and the United States has begun to indicate the sort of uses that may be found for forest products as fuel, structural material, and the raw material of chemical industry, as man's supplies of the fossil fuels and mineral resources become exhausted.

The possibilities of northern forests, great as they are, pale beside the possibilities of tropical forests, where the environment permits growth all of the year around, and where the long course of biological evolution has produced an endless array of different kinds of trees among which to search for products and qualities useful for human purposes. The forest represents the most efficient system so far found for using solar energy to convert carbon dioxide from the air, and water and minerals from the soil into cellulose, lignin, and hundreds of special chemicals on which ingenious man could base his economy.

Yet civilized man has hardly begun to study this forest. In the regions of the Amazon, the Congo or the East Indies it is still easy to find trees that haven't yet been given scientific names; and of the thousands of kinds that have been given scientific names, we know hardly more than the shape of the leaf and the structure of the flowers. Here, surely, is an endless frontier for the future.

When the scientist sits down and tries to visualize the possibilities for the future of man, he is dismissed by people at large for the good and sufficient reason that he is being "impractical." Or in another phraseology, he is not "facing reality." If we stop to analyze the situation, we find that this "reality" that the scientist ignores in his calculations is a very special thing. It does not lie in the processes of nature, which the scientist can calculate nicely and accurately, but in the processes of men, which have so far defeated his attempts at analysis and control. Reality, it appears, consists not of forests and oceans and human needs and possible chemical transformations, but of politics and pressure groups and manifest destinies and trade policies.

Personally, I think we have got all mixed up in this matter of reality, and that some day mankind will wake up and find that colonialism and nationalism and the imperial idea are all figments of a very nasty dream, resulting from an indigestion that was acquired at some period in the Stone Age. But whether or not our present reality represents a dream, we are living in it, and we ought to examine it as a part of our picture in the tropics. So, in the next chapter, we shall glance briefly at politics and government in the tropics, even though it means stepping through a looking glass into a world where you have to run very fast to stay where you are, and where words, after the fashion of Humpty Dumpty, mean just what you choose them to mean— neither more nor less.

CHAPTER XV

★

The Varieties of Tropical Government

I HAVE made a catalogue of 75 separate tropical governments—some of them representing independent, national sovereignties, some of them separately administered colonies. This must be about the minimum figure. I got it by eliminating countries with less than half of their area within the tropics (like Argentina and Pakistan) and by lumping the innumerable colonial administrations of the various Pacific Islands into eight rather arbitrary groups, and by a similarly highhanded reduction of the West Indian colonial administrations to three (British, French and American).

I have not calculated the total of governments for the world, to see what percentage lies within the tropics. I tried, but it soon became evident that the problem of deciding what is a separate "government" or "country" is really complicated, and that the arbitrary nature of any decision makes the figures quite meaningless. It is clear enough from a glance at the maps, though, that governments and countries are much more abundant in the tropics than elsewhere. Only western Europe makes a patchwork comparable with Africa or South America. Most of the rest of the Temperate Zone is covered by the monochrome areas of the Soviet Union, China, Canada, the United States and, in the south, Australia.

I do not mean to imply that the tropical countries are all small. Brazil is larger than the continental United States; and India, though less than half of this area, contains one sixth of the human population of the planet—almost as many people as the United States and the Soviet Union combined, though still considerably less than the presumed population of China.

I have been using "government" and "country" as though they were interchangeable words, though quite obviously they are not, since sometimes one country has several governments, while in other cases, several countries may have the same government. It is all part of this through-the-looking-glass atmosphere of human politics. In my list, for instance, I have one item for "French Indochina," though I suppose I might equally well have listed five countries—Cambodia, Laos, Annam, Cochin China and Tonkin. And this particular land area happens at the moment to be afflicted with two quite different governments, one under French colonial management, and one under the personal direction of a fellow called Ho chi-Minh.

This is no new or peculiar situation. Governments and countries have been appearing and disappearing, merging and separating in dizzily complex ways, since the beginning of recorded history. About the best one can do, at any given moment, is to trust to the insight of the Rand, McNally Company, and treat any distinctly colored area on their maps as a distinct "country," probably afflicted with a distinct "government."

The collection, isolation and recognition of governments, then, seems difficult enough; but this is child's play compared with the problems of classifying governments. Yet it is obvious enough that there are many different kinds—in fact, it seems on close examination that no two are alike, and this, perhaps, is the root of the difficulty.

Within the tropics, though, there are two basic classes of governments that differ sharply enough so that almost any specimen can be readily sorted into one category or the other. These are

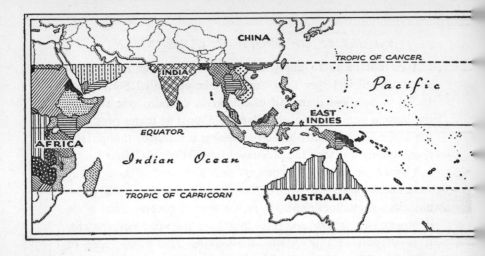

colonial governments and national governments—those in which the strings of government are manipulated from outside of the country, and the opposite, subject primarily to internal manipulation. This classification gets in trouble with "protectorates" and "spheres of influence" but these at the moment are not obvious on the tropical scene.

Curiously, both the colonial and the national ideas seem to be relatively new in human history—and perhaps all the more potent because of their newness.

"Colony" originally meant the settlement of subjects of a particular state (government) beyond the confines of their original area (country). Thus the Phoenicians established colonies in many parts of the Mediterranean, as a part of their trade network. And later the Greek city-states similarly established many colonies, though these were administratively independent, each colony thus an independent government. Macedonia and Rome, following patterns of contiguous conquest, really illustrate the imperial, rather than the colonial, idea; but in the Middle Ages, Genoa and Venice developed colonial systems, somewhat similar to the Phoenician, primarily as moves in the strategy of trade.

This is the meagre background for the colonial system that

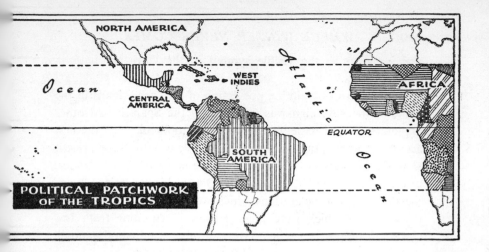

POLITICAL PATCHWORK OF THE TROPICS

developed after the geographical explosion of Europe in the 16th century. The Portuguese and the Spaniards triggered this explosion, and instigated the modern European concept of colonies. I suppose the idea of ever expanding conquest came naturally on the heels of their wars with the Moors, and in the face of the feeble and futile resistance of primitive peoples, "discovery" easily came to be equated with "conquest."

Certainly the idea of claiming possession of discovered territory appeared early in the history of the Portuguese voyages. Henry Hart remarks that the expedition of Diogo Cão in 1482, which reached the Congo, "marked the first employment of stone *padrões*. Each was a column surmounted by a cube terminating in a cross, and inscribed on one side with the arms of Portugal, together with the name of the king and that of the explorer and the date of discovery in Latin and/or Portuguese on the other. The use of these padrões was an idea of King John's. They were to be set up on prominent landmarks at various important places visited, with four objectives in view. First, they were a concrete proof that the discoverer had reached the place claimed by him; second, thereafter they would be invaluable as landmarks; third, they would be unquestioned proof of the priority of Portuguese discovery and sovereignty; and finally, surmounted by the cross, they were to be the visible symbol of the Christian faith in heathen lands."

This pattern of claiming possession of all "new" lands in the name of the sovereign was followed by the Spanish and other explorers. We all remember from our schoolbooks that the first act of Columbus, on October 12th, 1492, was to "take possession of said island, to which he gave the name of Sant Salvador, in the name of the King and of the Queen, his sovereigns, making the required declarations which were set down at length in the affidavits which were there prepared" (quoting from Las Casas). I suppose we would now call this a "unilateral action," though nobody seems to regard it as extraordinary.

The first direct contact between Europe and another civilized culture was the Portuguese arrival in India. There the Portuguese seem at first to have had only the idea of establishing trading stations, despite their belligerent relations with the Samorin of Calicut. This was partly because the Portuguese were at first under the misapprehension that the Indians were some kind of Christians, since they clearly were not Moslems. But the Indian-Portuguese relationship began inauspiciously, because of the cruelty and highhandedness of da Gama, and it soon became apparent that the maintenance of peaceful and friendly trading stations would be impossible. In 1505 Francesco d'Almeida was sent out with the title of Viceroy of India, and with full powers for establishing government, making treaties, regulating commerce, and waging war. He built a fort at Cannanore, thus starting the Portuguese attempt at exercising sovereignty in India (which still persists in the colony of Goa).

Portugal and Spain naturally came into conflict at once over this matter of sovereignty by right of discovery, and an attempt was made to settle the matter by the Treaty of Tordesillas, of June 7th, 1494, whereby, under the authority of Pope Alexander VI, a north-south line was drawn 370 leagues west of the Cape Verde Islands (which in our terms would be about 50° West of

Greenwich). All non-Christian lands discovered or to be discovered east of this line were to belong to Portugal, west of it, to Spain. This was subsequently the base of the Portuguese claim to Brazil.

This papal disposition of the non-Christian world was not automatically accepted: France, naturally, objected at being left out; and the Protestant colonial powers (which did not become colonial until after they became Protestant) never paid any attention to it. The relative Spanish and Portuguese positions in America, however, were consolidated by actual immigration, settlement, conquest and government. In the Old World, European settlement in the tropics hardly occurred, because the local people did not conveniently die off as the American Indians did, leaving empty space to be filled by European spill-over. The Eastern cultures also proved to be much more resistant to religious and political conversion. Such factors as these led to completely divergent patterns of colonial development in the various sections of the tropics.

The American colonies, then, became integral parts of the Spanish and Portuguese systems, held by bonds of race, language, and common institutions, as well as by force of conquest. The Asiatic colonies, however, were essentially mechanisms for channelling and monopolizing trade—they were, in fact, actually managed for a good part of the time by the trading companies of the various powers—and they passed from hand to hand in the course of the varying fortunes of war and diplomacy in Europe. No one paid much attention to tropical Africa until the 19th century, and then it, too, got split up in accordance with the vicissitudes of European diplomacy and for purposes of trade and exploitation, without any intention of permanent settlement.

I have, of course, greatly oversimplified in this sketch of the development of the colonial idea. The patchwork quilt of sovereignties that we see on a contemporary map of the tropical regions is the result of varied and complex forces. Some of these could be classed as economic; and many interpretations would make the economic forces dominant. This is clear enough in India and the East Indies, where the struggle for trade has always been uppermost. But Spanish colonial policy in America was also always dominated by economic motives, by theories of the advantages of monopoly of trade, of the necessity of suppressing colonial manufacture for the prosperity of the mother country. Even in the 20th-century colonial moves of powers like Germany and Italy, economic motives have always been alleged—the necessity for access to raw materials, the utility of a "captive market" for manufactured goods—though at the same time other economists have claimed that colonies were economic liabilities to the controlling powers.

But cultural forces have also been important: and the varied colonial patterns of America, Africa, Asia and the Pacific can be more readily interpreted in cultural than in economic terms.

Behind all of this lies the background of the development of Western culture itself: of the vicissitudes of power and politics among the warring Western nations, of the development of various national ideas and ambitions, of the ever increasing preoccupation with national prestige. I have a tendency to blame all of the troubles of the world on this one factor of "nationalism," though it is clear enough that the world had plenty of the same kind of troubles before anyone had thought of the national idea, so that blaming nationalism today would be like blaming religion in the 15th century or imperialism in the 1st century, or just plain human cussedness in 5,000 B.C. Still, nationalism is the most obvious form of human cussedness in the 20th century and it is a Western invention that has been enthusiastically adopted in the tropics; so some inquiry into the matter here may be appropriate.

Nationalism is generally considered to be an invention of the late 18th century, though of course its roots can be traced far back in human history. Tribal loyalty is surely as ancient as tribe formation, and with the advent of agriculture and complex social organization, this would become transformed into community loyalty. Community solidarity is probably still the strongest political force over most of the non-Western world. The government, the nation or the state would have no meaning, for instance, to the average villager of India, who sees the world at large only in terms of its impact on his own community. This has been described very well in a little book by the Wisers, called *Behind Mud Walls.*

The city becomes too large and complex for this sort of tribal or community loyalty, and allegiance is probably early transferred to the symbols of government or the persons of leaders. These leaders, as they became monarchs, kings, emperors, seem to have depended primarily on the organization and loyalty of their entourages for the maintenance of their government and territory, rather than on the development of supercommunity loyalties in the people at large. The Greek city-states, of course, seem to have developed loyalties of an almost national sort, as did the citizenry of Rome, but Roman citizenship, at any rate, developed as a thing-in-itself, not conditioned or moulded by rival citizenships.

The Roman idea got supplanted in the Middle Ages by the feudal system, with its loyalties to persons. Columbus claimed San Salvador not in the name of Spain, but in the name of his King and Queen; and the whole Western philosophy, down through the 18th century, seems to have been to consolidate loyalty around a sovereignty or dynasty, rather than around any national idea.

It is often said that the big impulse to nationalism came from the French revolution. It was the revolutionaries who made the deliberate effort to substitute loyalty to *la patrie* for loyalty to king; and that they succeeded so completely showed that, in this respect, they were in accord with the trend of their age. They attempted to establish a uniform national language, national religion, national education, customs and institutions, to glorify the national flag, and to inculcate in every Frenchman the willingness to die not for his king, but for his country. The French revolution gave way to Napoleon and to the power balances of the Treaty of Vienna, but the blaze of nationalism had been set, and it has gone sweeping on with ever increasing intensity through the ensuing years.

I am oversimplifying again, of course. The United States might be considered as an earlier embodiment of the national idea than France, but the intellectual forces that led to the two revolutions were in part the same, and I do not think that nationalism gained a virulent, religious force in the United States until after the Civil War. And American nationalism had no impact on the tropics until the time of the Spanish War, when the United States halfheartedly and rather ashamedly started copying current European fashions. We never have been able to make up our minds about nationalism and colonialism, which leads to all kinds of complications in our relations to other peoples.

The national idea caught on readily enough in tropical America, so that the Spanish colonial system broke up almost at once into some 17 national states (to which Cuba was added later). The leaders of the revolutionary movement, like Bolívar, had hoped for some more general, unified American system, but the forces tending toward disintegration were too strong. The national idea, both in Europe and in Latin America, got solidified into units whose size was determined by the systems of communication and transportation that were available around 1800. By the next century, when methods of communication might have made a unified Spanish America possible, the national idea had become so firmly implanted as to make any union seem utterly impractical, despite its obvious advantage from every point of view except the maintenance of nationalism.

The national diversity of Spanish America, and the strength of the national idea there, never cease to astonish me. With a

uniform language, uniform religion, uniform historical background over such a large area, you would think that the cohe-
sive forces would be stronger than the disruptive ones. There
are, to be sure, racial differences, like the predominance of
Indians in Mexico, Guatemala, Peru, Ecuador and Bolivia, and
the larger Negro element in some countries than in others; and
there are considerable differences in topography, climate and
resources among the different countries. But my impression is
that the national differences among the countries are not so
much a result of these racial and environmental differences, as
the result of the imposition of frontier barriers, which have
forced each country to follow a more or less independent line
of development.

Some of these countries have had an almost continuous history of political turbulence, with dictatorship, revolutions, wars
and insurrections following each other in a constant stream.
Others—Costa Rica is always cited as the example—have had
an almost continuous history of peace and stable, elective government. All of them have modeled their governments on the
republican form, more or less after the fashion of the United
States. But this republican form was grafted on a heritage of
Spanish autocratic control and of Spanish legal tradition, and the.
result has not always seemed fortunate. Actual control of the
government has often stayed in the hands of the wealthy, land-
owning families, and these have naturally manipulated the forms
to their own advantage. These wealthy people are charming,
cultivated, and endowed with the best of intentions; but this very
background makes them conservative, dubious of external influences and of internal unrest, sharing thus the characteristics of
landed aristocracies everywhere. Popular revolt has often merely
created a new set of political leaders who have assumed dicta-
torial powers and have perhaps started to institute reforms but
who, in the end, have succumbed to the blandishments of the
aristocracies and thus become absorbed into the old ruling group.

I do not know what should be done about this, if anything. Certainly the United States, when it intervenes, seems to succeed only in causing damage, from every point of view. The thing that bothers me is not so much the form of government, as the weight of the national idea. Almost every one of these countries has a vastly greater budget for the army than for education, though I fail to see why any Latin American government needs an army. The frontiers also impose a heavy burden on travel, trade and communication, often cutting quite arbitrarily across natural trade routes, as in the case of the Amazon and Orinoco river systems.

One of the most vicious effects of nationalism, I think, lies in the compartmentation of human thought. Mankind as a whole is not too large a stage for philosophy, science and the arts; and any narrow, national stage is hopelessly crippling. I have thought most about this in connection with science which, in its modern development, has been truly international. The scientists of Europe somehow largely escaped the enveloping nationalism of the 19th century; and if you try to trace back the development of any idea or discovery, you find that you cross back and forth, in the most helter-skelter fashion, from Germany to England to France to Italy to Denmark and, latterly, to the United States. The cross-fertilization of ideas completely ignored nationality, even through the first World War, and only lately have the nationalists come to exalt German science, and Russian science, and (God help us) American science.

This national compartmentation is, I think, an important reason for the failure of Latin America to contribute its fair share to the development of modern science, as I pointed out in the last chapter.

The national idea has not made so much progress in Asia, though it is being actively enough developed now by various ruling groups, both local and foreign. We tried to make a national state out of the Philippines, and the Indonesians are trying to create one for themselves. Whether India and Pakistan will ever turn out to be states after the Western model, I do not know. India, as a whole, is more comparable to Europe in its linguistic and cultural diversity than to any single Western nation, and it may be difficult to develop there the more vicious nationalistic traits, though the belligerence between the dominions of Pakistan and India would seem to furnish a good start.

What will happen in Indochina is anybody's guess, and I am probably about the least qualified of persons to venture any prediction. But it is curious that the French, who were pretty much responsible for the nationalist idea in the first place, have a particularly bloody record of suppressing nationalism in other people; and they seem determined to maintain some kind of authority in Indochina as long as they can. French domination in Indochina is not very ancient, except for Cochin China, which was long a colony; the "protectorates" over the other states date from the late 19th century.

Siam, alone among the countries of tropical Asia, managed to escape Western domination, partly because neither France nor England was willing to let the other gain ascendancy there, and partly because of the skill of its 19th century kings, who played the game of Western diplomacy with nice calculation. It has lately changed its name to an older form, Thailand, and adopted a constitution which makes it a "limited" rather than an "absolute" monarchy.

I wish I could make comparisons between, say, Siam, Burma, Annam and Java, to bring out the effect of the various sorts of European contacts on local development; but such comparisons, without firsthand acquaintance, would be meaningless. It certainly looks as though the Siamese had not been damaged by escaping European dominance, even though they have not taken advantage of their independence to build themselves into a "power."

The history of government in tropical Asia during the period of Western domination seems a bloody mess, reflecting no credit on the West. The Western excuse, of course, is that during this period a certain amount of peace and internal security has been imposed, which has permitted a more orderly development of the various countries. When one reads the general history of the region, this gains in plausibility. The behavior of the Portuguese, Dutch, British and French seems less awful when compared with the events of the preceding centuries, with the various invasions of the Aryans, Arabs, Huns, Afghans, and Chinese, and the constant warfare of the innumerable principalities, racial groups, and occasional empires. These internal wars were frozen for a couple of hundred years, or subordinated to the warrings of the European powers. The danger is that now, with the European hold loosened, they will break out again.

It is difficult to see how the West can help Asia toward achieving political stability until it has solved its own problems of national rivalries and national hatreds. But in this present world, reduced to neighborhood size by modern communication and transportation, we cannot ignore Asia's problems, any more than Asia can ignore ours; though on both sides we have a long way to go before we can achieve anything that might be labeled "understanding."

We should round out this review of tropical governments with some remarks about Africa. My ignorance of Africa is only exceeded by my ignorance of Asia, so I shall not try to produce any profound thoughts about either. Africa ought, however, to have the serious attention of any student of government. There it is, a great, populous continent, split up into an arbitrary patchwork of European "colonies," except for the tiny "republic" of Liberia and the larger "empire" of Ethiopia, so recently coughed up by the Italians.

These African colonies are not European settlements, like the colonies in America and Australia, nor are they conquered local kingdoms, like the colonies of Asia. An exception to this latter statement would be Madagascar, which was conquered by the French in 1895 in much the same way as Ethiopia was more recently conquered by the Italians—only the French happened to be in fashion, acting at a time when all of the Western powers were grabbing whatever they could.

What is the future of this colonial system? The West in recent years has repeatedly emphasized its adherence to the principle of self-government for all peoples. But how can this be implemented in the case of Africa?

It is difficult to find any very concrete indications that the West takes its ideas of "freedom" seriously in regard to Africa, or that any of the Western powers are anxious to stop playing at master in these equatorial dominions. Such policies as have developed differ for each colonial power. The French, I believe, hope eventually to make their African colonies an integral part of the French national state—aiming at the sort of arrangement that has actually been achieved in Algeria. They thus have encouraged a certain amount of intermarriage, and in 1941 they appointed a Negro, Felix Sylvestre Eboué, to the important post of Governor General of French Equatorial Africa. But Eboué was not a local man; he was from French Guiana.

The British aim vaguely at some eventual independent, dominion status, in some very distant future, when the natives have got educated to the onerous burdens of self-government; and halting starts have been made in this educational process. The Belgians and Portuguese seem not to have worried about eventual aims, and get along with the day-by-day process of exploitation as best they can.

This pattern of nationalisms, projected onto Africa, is obvious nonsense, and hardly likely to work smoothly for any long period into the future. But at the moment there seem to be no alternatives. If and when the West manages to achieve a non-national governmental system, a United Nations of some sort that can really act as a force for the suppression of armed strife throughout the world, the development of Africa will probably become an international responsibility. But the West has a lot of problems of its own to solve before that day is reached.

Which is, I think, enough about governments. I have tried to give some idea of the diversity of republics, dictatorships, crown colonies, dominions, appendages of the French Colonial Office, sultanates, and empires that afflict the zone between Capricorn and Cancer, because I think it is as important to study these as it is to study the climate, if conditions in the tropics are to be understood. Governments, it seems to me, are much more difficult to study than climates, so I have had no hope of making any contribution beyond emphasizing the fact that governments are there, in all of their variety, the product of historical and geographical events—and also a contributing cause to those events. They are proper material for dissection by the social scientists; though the fellow with the scalpel had better be careful, because governments can bite.

CHAPTER XVI

★

The Planetary Neighborhood

IT is no wonder that we have difficulty in adjusting our systems of government, our trade relations, and our ideas to
the realities of the world today. Our social and economic
systems have developed gradually, over thousands of years, on a
planet where distance has kept a fairly constant meaning; then,
in the short space of less than a hundred years, distance has lost
its meaning. Distance, as H. G. Wells said, has been abolished.
It is not surprising that it takes us a little while to adjust to this
extraordinary, new situation.

For most of human history, distance has been measurable in
terms of walking men; and our diverse cultures and civilizations,
races and languages have been developed within this frame.
Mankind, by walking, has covered a lot of territory. Man must
have spread completely over the habitable parts of the continental masses of Asia, Africa and Europe very early in his evolu-
tionary history. He got to America via the Behring Strait region,
which may have been dry land 25,000 years ago, allowing him
to walk across from Asia; or, since man early took to making
small boats, he may have got across by island hopping, and then
started out on the long trek to Tierra del Fuego, which surely
took some thousands of years to reach.

With boats, man was able to extend his range to the islands

of the seas and to move more easily along the waterways and coasts of the continents. Land movement remained chained by the speed of walking men, but with sea movements, we have the record of a slow and gradual evolution in the arts of shipbuilding, sailing and navigation which finally made the seas the primary avenues of human intercourse during the period of modern history.

Man on land, of course, learned to use horses and camels, to build highways, and to establish stagecoach routes and post relays; but these show little progressive change through recorded history in speed of communication because the most important element, highway construction, was mastered early. There was no appreciable improvement on the systems of land communication developed by the Romans and the Incas until about a hundred years ago, when railways and telegraphs came into use. The propaganda and the armies of the Pharoahs, of Alexander, of the Romans, of Napoleon, moved with about the same speed and facility. And this provided the frame within which our systems of social organization and of cultural diversity were built up.

About a hundred years ago, distance started to change its meaning in a dizzy fashion, with the use of railways, telegraphs, marine cables, steamships, telephones, automobiles, airplanes and radios. The planet, in this short time, became a neighborhood; the world's problems became neighborhood problems; and the great question of our time is whether the world's peoples can find some way of learning to be good neighbors.

Along with the change in the scale of distance, we have an equally extraordinary change in the scale of power. The two are indissolubly linked; and together, I think they make it inevitable that whatever human civilization survives will be a global civilization. Nations, races, cultures, political systems, have all lost the context in which they so painfully and so slowly developed: the context of distance in terms of walking or sailing man; and the context of power in terms of simple multiples of animal and human muscle. Out of this context, these ideas have lost their significance; and we must either give them a new significance, or invent new ideas that correspond to the present realities.

This does not mean that I think all men must become alike in order to learn to live together peacefully on the shrunken planet; nor do I think that differences in race, culture, or even political systems are likely to disappear. After all, no neighborhood is uniform: there are always the fussy Joneses and the slovenly Browns, and the Blacks who have never asked the Whites to dinner. Nor is any nation uniform, nor any particular civilization. Peaceful relations among the diverse elements of a neighborhood depend not on uniformity, but on tolerance—tolerance within the limits of actions that are not clearly inimical to the neighborhood welfare. And the suppression of inimical actions depends not on individuals, but on the community, on the Joneses, Browns, Blacks and Whites all acting together.

Neighborhood tolerance clearly is a complex affair. Mere nearness and familiarity are not enough to breed tolerance—they may, in fact, exacerbate differences and breed hatreds. It is easy enough to think of examples of this among families, tribes and nations; and from this, we can be sure that the abolition of distance on our planet will not necessarily, in itself, result in any increase in tolerance among its nations or diverging cultures.

Something more than nearness and familiarity is needed— something that I would call understanding, understanding not only of our neighbors, but of ourselves, of what we are and how we got that way. This is no easy job. It will take hard work, patience, ingenuity and a great deal of time, which all go together to make up the process that we call education.

In this book, then, I have been trying to make a contribution toward this neighborhood understanding. My subject has been the tropical region: its natural features, its human inhabitants, and the relationships between the two. I have also written a great deal about Western civilization, since I am a product of that civilization, writing for my fellows, and since the impact of that civilization has everywhere altered conditions in the tropics today.

My comments on the West have not always been flattering, but I think that self-criticism is an important element in this process of building up neighborhood understanding. And however satisfactory Western ways of life may be in their own environmental context, I have come more and more to suspect that they are not, in their entirety, adapted to the different environmental conditions of the tropics. This is obvious enough in superficial things like clothing and housing; but the superficial maladaptations may be indications of some more fundamental difficulty.

Western civilization is clearly a remarkable affair. It is too complex for me to analyse, and I have no idea what caused it, why it thrived, or what will happen to it. I fail, however, to see any simple cause and effect relationships, like climate or race, and I doubt whether there is any simple explanation of the genesis of any civilization. I am quite sure that human intellectual achievement is not dependent on temperature lines, however much its direction may be governed by such climatic factors. And I am equally sure that civilization is not dependent on any particular variety of racial intelligence—again even though its direction may possibly be influenced by racial characteristics, though I know of no evidence demonstrating this.

Whatever the origin of the West, there is nothing we can do about it, any more than we can rewrite the history of the early Western contact with the tropics. The anthropologist often sounds as though he wished all of his nice, exotic cultures could be carefully preserved, protected from the contaminating and disintegrating influences of the West. The historian, similarly, often seems to regret the actions that he describes, whose consequences can now easily be seen in the problems of today. But the historical actions and the established cultural relations are our given data, with which we must now work, and there is no use in wasting time in wishing that the given circumstances were different, in trying to set back the clock.

The West has established a global economy, and this also is a given datum. It has come to depend on a whole range of tropical products as basic essentials of its industrial system and the whole world has got involved with its network of trade and finance, as well as with its ideas. The West could not retreat, even if it wanted to; so that continuing economic and cultural contacts are inevitable, unless the global system collapses.

But the present perilous state of relationship among the peoples of the planetary neighborhood shows that this Western contact with the tropics cannot be maintained on an exploitative basis: that the tropical peoples cannot be kept tributary in either an economic or a political sense, which means that the West must modify its traditional methods of action. These considerations are valid quite aside from the present tensions between the West and the Russian system, though these tensions make it even more urgent that the West establish reciprocal relations with the tropical peoples, and not leave them with the feeling that they might as well try jumping from the frying pan into the fire.

This is plain enough, and widely enough realized. It is reflected in the shifting policies of the British Empire, in the preoccupation of the United Nations with the problems of technological aid among nations, and in the plans of the United States to implement the famous "Point Four" of President Truman's inaugural address. The President, in making this point, said:

"We must embark on a bold new program for making the benefits of our scientific advances and our industrial progress available for the improvement and growth of under-developed areas. . . . We should make available to peace-loving peoples the benefits of our store of technical knowledge in order to help them realize their aspirations for a better life. And, in cooperation with other nations, we should foster capital investment in areas needing development. Our aim should be to help the free peoples of the world, through their own efforts, to produce more food, more clothing, more materials for housing, and more mechanical power to lighten their burdens."

This sounds grand, and I am sure it was set forth with a spirit that corresponds to its broad and friendly wording; that it reflects a realization of the urgencies arising from man's present global systems of economy and communication. It reflects also a fundamental attitude that has long characterized the American people: a desire to be helpful, a sort of missionary spirit on the national scale, a preoccupation with the ideals that arose from the ferment of their own revolution.

This attitude lay behind the famous doctrine that was enunciated by President Monroe in 1823. It was the spiritual drive behind our war with Spain, even though this enterprise, in its actual development, got perverted into a sort of an imperialist junket. This attitude found expression in the fourteen points of President Wilson, which was transmuted into the cynical compromises and muddled politics of Versailles. President Roosevelt again gave expression to this attitude in developing his policy of the "good neighbor," and it colors all of our recent statements of national policy and international intentions.

Our intentions, certainly, are good, by any general standard of evaluation. But these good intentions often seem to end up as bigger and better paving stones on that broad highway leading toward hell. With this experience, it seems to me that it is always in order to examine both our intentions and our implementation of those intentions; and these are germane to the subject of the present book, insofar as they involve American policy in the tropical areas.

I quoted the text of President Truman's "fourth point" from a release of the Department of State, and this release contains also a map of the world which shows the stages of development of the different regions. The "developed areas," on this map, include the United States, Canada, Australia, New Zealand and most of Europe. Italy, Spain and the Balkans are separated from the rest of Europe as "intermediate"; and the Soviet Union, South Africa, Argentina and Chile are also marked as "intermediate." This leaves the broad band of the tropics as "undeveloped," with a northward extension in Asia to include Afghanistan, China and Japan.

The more I look at this map, the more puzzling it seems: to mark Italy as "intermediate" and yet boldly to include the whole of Australia and Alaska as "developed." It seems even more curious to mark Japan as "undeveloped"—I would have thought that Japan had recently given a demonstration of being rather overdeveloped.

The only conclusion I can draw from this map is that "developed" means "Westernized." The exclusion of Italy and Spain seems at first anomalous from this point of view, since they were the leaders of the Western world a few centuries ago. But I suppose they are considered to have slid backward in modern times as the Western center of gravity moved northward to England, Germany and France.

If "developed" means "Westernized," I suppose "development" means "Westernization," and with this translation both our intentions and our policy take on a somewhat different color. Particularly with regard to the tropics, we have reason to pause and consider the nature of our endeavor. We come back to the general problem of the "white man's burden" which seems to me to be the weight of his own civilization, loaded down with elements that in the tropical environment become merely handicaps, whatever value they may have had in the environment where they were developed. In attempting to Westernize tropical peoples, we may actually be trying to transfer a similar burden to them, so that it is no wonder that the process does not meet with any great success.

The United States has been trying very hard to develop Puerto Rico and the Philippines for fifty years now, sending them experts and capital in much the same way that we now propose to send experts and capital to all tropical peoples. Yet Puerto Rico and the Philippines are still regarded by our government as "undeveloped" if I read my map correctly. And if, after almost five hundred years of contact with the Western world, the whole wide band of the tropics can still be marked as undeveloped, un-Westernized, may it not be that there is something wrong with the attitudes and methods of the West, with the nature of Western civilization itself when placed in this environment?

What, then, should we do? Since I have raised the problem and criticised our present methods of meeting it, I should have some alternative, some pet formula, ready to pull out of my pocket.

I doubt whether there is any simple answer. It is a gain, I think, merely to pose the problem because it may lead us to examine ourselves as well as our tropical neighbors, and this is healthy because neighborhood tolerance is going to depend on understanding ourselves as well as understanding our neighbors. Quite obviously, we shall have to go through a reciprocal learning process—we can't just be the teachers.

This will be very slow. Also, clearly, long-term action will depend on political developments, on the West finding substitutes for its ideas of nationalism and colonialism, on the development of some global concept of sovereignty and some mechanism for the maintenance of world order and peace. This, too, may be disastrously slow. And in the meanwhile there are always the immediate problems, that must be met with immediate action, and here neighborhood helpfulness of the sort envisioned by President Truman may be essential. We must remember, however, that neighborly assistance, if it is to be effective, must be carried out with consummate tact and understanding, including an understanding of our own limitations.

Beyond this, I do have a pet formula; and as might be expected, it corresponds with the direction of my special interests. Just as Western theologians consider that the way to salvation lies through Christianity, and Western politicians that it lies through democracy, and Western industrialists that it lies through the fostering of manufacturing plants, so I consider that the way to salvation for the tropics lies through science.

The West, in its attempts to help in the development of the tropics, has been working at the level of technology. And this, it seems to me, is the wrong level. The technologies have been developed under particular sets of circumstances, and they are often surprisingly limited by those circumstances. But the technologies of the modern world are the somewhat incidental products of basic science, and this science is the very root of the peculiar genius of the West and thus constitutes so far the West's most important contribution to the sum of human progress.

Almost everyone likes the technologies of the modern Western world. The tropical peoples (or their governments, at least) are all anxious to have the benefits of medicine, scientific agriculture, electrification, and all of the thousands of gadgets that have come into everyday Western use; and the West is sincerely anxious to help them get these things, from whatever mixture of motives. But the attempts at exporting the technologies do not impress me as having been very successful. Sometimes they have simply failed to catch on. Sometimes they have led to unexpected and disastrous consequences, as with the population explosion resulting from the successful imposition of public health in Puerto Rico. Sometimes they have led to the concentration of power in the hands of groups uneducated in the responsibilities of power. Often our technologies have been useless, or dangerous, or ineffectual, without the basic science from which they arose. We have got the cart before the horse, and then we are puzzled because the contraption does not work.

Unfortunately, it is much easier to export technology than it is to export science. It is difficult to say what science is, to determine the factors that led to its development in Western civilization, or to untangle the complex ways in which this basic science has led to the proliferation of all of the varied technologies that give the Western world its present character. Yet some understanding of all of these things would seem to be essential to the development of methods of aiding the establishment of science among other peoples or in other cultures.

What is science, anyway? Definition is not easy, and any two scientists are liable to differ considerably when they get involved in attempts at definition. I think that James Bryant Conant has made the best analysis so far of the nature of science in his book, *Science and Common Sense,* and I am using the word here with the meaning given it by Conant; but I know of no way of acquiring an understanding of this meaning except through reading Conant's own book. His definition, which seems naked and austere without its clothing of illustration and explanation, is that "science is an interconnected series of concepts and conceptual schemes that have developed as a result of experimentation and observation and are fruitful of further experimentation and observations."

Science, in this sense, seems to be a special product of Western civilization, though its roots can be traced easily enough to the Greeks, to the Hindus and to the early Arabic civilization. I have spent a deal of time wondering why this modern development of science should be so peculiarly Western, but I have not come up with any simple explanation. I suspect that it has resulted mostly from a union between the philosopher and the artisan that started to be formed somewhere around the fifteenth and sixteenth centuries, and that was peculiar to Western Europe.

The artisans of all human societies have become skilled in handling their materials, and through their observations and experiments, they have come across all sorts of ways of changing and improving their techniques. But the process has been slow, sporadic and uncertain, because the artisans have not been interested in anything beyond their immediate tasks. They were trying to make pots or build houses or handle metals, and they were interested in getting the job done rather than in building up conceptual schemes.

Conceptual schemes have always been the concern of the philosophers, and philosophers are notoriously unreliable in the practical matters of everyday life. They tend to rise above such things, and to spend their time chasing the eternal verities or trying to reduce an incoherent universe into something that can be comprehended by the human mind. The philosopher and the artisan must often have worked together in times past, to produce the elaborate calendars, the navigation aids, and the everyday rituals of antiquity. But the tendency toward specialization in the early civilizations resulted in an ever widening gap between the workman and the thinker.

I cannot isolate any particular pressure that led the philosopher to become concerned with the problems of the artisan in the middle ages of Western Europe. It may have been some characteristic of the social structure of the Italian cities; it may have been associated somehow with the problems that arose as civilization moved into more difficult climatic environments; it may have resulted from the failure of the slave supply and other aspects of the disintegrating economy of post-Roman times. The union was certainly not sudden and complete, and to this day we find that some individual scientists are mostly concerned with thought, with theory; and others with action, with experiment. But the two have somehow arrived at and maintained a common understanding that has been exceedingly fruitful.

The obvious fruitfulness has been in the new technologies that have so transformed the nature of human relationships on our planetary surface. These technologies present Western society itself with many internal problems whose solutions are far from clear. The internal problems are in part similar to or identical with the external problems: whether, for instance, the methods and attitudes of science are applicable to studies of human society and behavior; or how, otherwise, we are going to develop social controls that correspond with the present material realities. But these are general problems of mankind and not peculiar to the tropics—our present subject of concern.

The technologies are surprisingly closely bound up with the general nature of Western civilization itself; they are, as the anthropologists would say, "culture bound." My book is full of examples, but it may be well to repeat some of them here. Our agriculture is preoccupied with the crops and crop methods of Europe and North America. Technicians, with this background, are apt to say that most tropical soils are "poor." But how can the substratum that produces the rain forest, the most massive and complex vegetable growth known on our planet, be called "poor soil"? It is different, surely, from the soil of Illinois, and will probably have to be managed after some very different fashion, for very different crops, perhaps through learning to operate in accord with the natural forces that have produced the forest, and through learning to utilize products of a forest economy. But this is a long, slow job that cannot be taught by some foreign expert who, until yesterday, had never seen a rain forest.

The techniques of Western medicine are equally culture bound. We have learned to control epidemic diseases, to change living patterns, to master infections and to improve diet, so that a child, at birth, can reasonably be expected to reach a ripe old age. But this has developed within a cultural pattern where births were becoming steadily less frequent through a variety of causes that we do not wholly understand. When these medical techniques are imported, as things-in-themselves, into a culture where the other factors are not operating, we may end up with a multiplication of misery despite our good intentions, as seems to have happened in Puerto Rico.

In more specific instances, we get worried about hookworm,

and try to persuade everyone to wear shoes—with consequences that I have already elaborated on. Our nutritionists have built up their system on the basis of Western food materials, and they will never, as outsiders, be able to go through the catalogue of tropical nature to work out the relationships of local foods: these must somehow be developed from local knowledge, arising from local needs.

Our heavy industry developed primarily through the exploitation of supplies of coal in close juxtaposition to supplies of iron ore, and so through the whole catalogue of Western industrial development. Surely industrialization in the tropics will have to depend on equally clever utilization of local advantages, which will depend on the drive of local needs and local comprehension of possibilities.

We must have an interchange of knowledge, surely, and much travel back and forth of experts of all varieties, sizes and colors. That is an almost inevitable consequence of the reduction of our planet to its neighborhood proportions; and it is precisely on this free flow of knowledge and persons that the health and continuing development of the scientific process depends. But it cannot be a one-way flow of Western experts telling the tropical peoples how to do things. The tropical peoples must take their place among the clique of scholars in our neighborhood—and I should not be greatly surprised if, in the end, they were not the leaders, as they were in the beginning.

I think there are ways in which the West could help to foster the development of basic science within the tropics. We have seen something of this within the United States itself. It is only in rather recent years that the United States has ceased to be tributary, in an intellectual sense, to Europe, and has started to pull its own weight in the advancement of science. This change, according to one line of reasoning, can be traced to the establishment of a very few institutions which were deliberately planned for the furtherance of basic science—places in the first instance like the Johns Hopkins, the University of Chicago and Leland Stanford, which led directly and rapidly to the development of other neighboring public and private universities into great institutions of learning.

My argument from this is that we might help the tropics most —and thus in the long run help ourselves—if we would export capital not only for things like industrialization, but for the establishment of local institutions of basic science in a few key places on a grand scale. The scholars may not be there now, but after all, in tropical economy, there is no present place for them. The United States had few important scientists until it had the institutions where they could be housed (and fed and exercised). And with provision for the basic science, the technologies would take care of themselves.

No single point of attack, of course, will solve the problems of any human community. The development of universities is tied up with the development of education in general; the support of universities is tied up with the general problems of the economy of a country. In the pattern of human life everything is interrelated in complex, puzzling and often indirect ways. But if we are going to initiate changes, we have to start somewhere. It seems to be as inevitable with man to try to initiate change as it is to try to resist change, so I have no doubt but what Western man, individually and collectively, will continue to try to initiate changes in the tropics. And given this, and given his long history of relative failure at the levels of technology and politics, I should at least like to see such an experiment in the establishment of basic science tried.

Aside from the problems of trying to help tropical man take his proper place in our planetary neighborhood, we have the drive of our own curiosity and of our own need to find out more about this tropical environment that girdles our earth. Western man has gone there mostly as an exploiter, as a trader, occasionally merely as a traveler and a tourist; but always he has gone weighed down with the burden of his own queer civilization. He got this civilization when he learned to wear fitted clothes and to build weatherproof houses where he could produce heat and light to overcome the barbaric environment north of the Alps. With these paraphernalia, he devised a way of life that certainly contains many admirable things that will contribute to the happiness and welfare of mankind everywhere. But it does not all go together in one package that can be used everywhere; and as a package, it is wrapped up in arrogance and sealed with intolerance. Maybe we can break it open and, taking only what we need, go to the tropics as students, to learn what we can there of nature and of man. For certainly there is much to learn.

Notes and Documentation

Under this heading I want to gather the sort of material that would ordinarily be dispersed in footnotes to the text. Such notes are very useful, in that they give an author the opportunity to cite sources, to point out reservations and qualifications, and to make digressions that are not directly relevant to the course of the argument. But they may be a considerable nuisance for the reader if, like me, he cannot resist glancing down to the bottom of the page each time he comes across an asterisk or superscript figure. Perhaps I can retain the virtues of footnotes, and avoid their inconvenience by assembling the material here as a running text to make a single, gigantic footnote to the whole book.

I have included, in the reference list, only publications in the English language, because the few other sources that I have used would be well known to scholars, and would not be easily available to the general reader. There is, in particular, a large and useful literature on the tropics in German; and the only book I know comparable in intent and scope to the one I have attempted here is Karl Sapper's little volume entitled *Die Tropen: Natur und Mensch zwischen den Wendekreisen*. In general, I have tried to indicate my most important sources during the actual writing of the book, and to cite reviews that in their turn contain useful bibliographies of special subjects. Journal articles covering original research have been listed only in a few instances where such reference seemed necessary to support points raised in the text.

The basic determinant of the limitations of my reference list, of course, is my own ignorance. I cannot pretend to a scholarly knowledge of any of the general topics that I have covered (except where mosquitoes are concerned) and the materials that I have used and cited have often been determined by accident: by the fact that a book happened to be on my own shelves, or happened to catch my eye while I was browsing in the stacks of some library. I am very conscious, then, of the fact that in attempting to provide documentation, I am only exposing my own inadequacy. But that, after all, is a

277

real function of documentation. To the scholar, the reference list will reveal omissions and weaknesses; while to the newcomer, it may open new paths for exploration.

CHAPTER I. THE POINT OF VIEW

Our eight years in Colombia, during which many of the ideas expressed in this book were developed, have been described by my wife (Nancy Bates, 1947). My concepts of the ecological, or natural history, point of view, were developed in a previous book (M. Bates, 1950).

CHAPTER II. THE ELEMENT OF HISTORY

The standard reference on Greek geography is Bunbury (1883). I have also depended on Wright (1925), who gives many notes on the Greeks, even though primarily concerned with later times. Brown (1949) has written a readable history of map-making. All of these contain detailed bibliographies. The Portuguese role in the geographical expansion of Europe has been summarized by Hart (1950). The quotation is from pp. 230–231 of Hart's book; it has been rather arbitrarily selected from among the numerous similar incidents that characterized the Portuguese voyages.

I have elaborated on Portuguese exploration rather than Spanish, because it is less well known. A good general account of the Spanish conquest of the Caribbean has been given by Means (1935). Any reading on exploration should include the anthology of Stefansson (1947), containing notes by the editor which, for me, put many things in a fresh perspective. The book by Outhwaite (1935) contains a series of charts that show graphically the progress of this exploration. The best study that I know of the impact of explorers and their followers on native peoples is contained in the book by Oliver (1951) which came to hand after my manuscript had been completed.

Von Hagen (1945) has given an account of four of the scientific explorers of the tropics (La Condamine, Humboldt, Darwin and Spruce); and Cutright (1940) has reviewed the material on naturalists in South America. Scientific knowledge of African problems has been reviewed by Worthington (1938) and scientific exploration in

Indonesia has been covered in a book edited by Honig and Verdoorn (1945). The accounts of the explorers themselves, however, remain the most interesting reading; and at the risk of being obvious, I have listed among the references the books by Darwin (1839), Wallace (1869), H. W. Bates (1864) and Belt (1874).

CHAPTER III. THE VARIETIES OF TROPICAL MAN

Here I have depended primarily on Hooton (1947) and Kroeber (1948). The latter book is not to be taken up for light reading on a summer afternoon, but it seems to me one of the great intellectual achievements of our time, arriving at a balanced synthesis of all of the puzzling and diverse trends of modern anthropological thought. On the subject of evolution in general and human evolution in particular, I can only recommend that the reader take up Simpson (1949). In writing this and the following chapters I have often checked with various anthropology texts, particularly Herskovits (1948) and Montagu (1945).

The subject of races has been covered from the point of view of modern genetics by Boyd (1950). Coon, Garn and Birdsell (1950) have recently reviewed the general subject in a book in which 30 distinct human races are named and described. The problems of racial classification in the Pacific are nicely outlined by Oliver (1951). The anthropological point of view towards the *Kon-Tiki* book (Heyerdahl, 1950) has been stated by Alphonse Riesenfeld in the "Letters" column of the magazine *Natural History* for February, 1951 (vol. 60, p. 50).

CHAPTER IV. THE VARIETIES OF TROPICAL CULTURE

For a general review of the concept of culture, Kluckhohn (1949) is easier to read than Kroeber or the other anthropology texts. My account of food-gathering peoples is based on Forde (1934), who has written a good ecological survey of the less complex varieties of human culture. The relationships among the different kinds of non-literate economies have been discussed by Herskovits (1940). The early history of tool-making and other technologies has been covered by Lips (1949).

With regard to the problems of the origin of agriculture, I have probably gained more from occasional conversations with two outstanding personalities, Professor Carl Sauer of the University of California and Professor Paul Mangelsdorf of Harvard, than from all of my reading. Unfortunately, neither of these men has written a general book on the origins of agriculture; but the flavor of their ideas can be gathered from Sauer (1950) and Mangelsdorf and Reeves (1939).

CHAPTER V. THE INCIDENCE OF CIVILIZATION

The history of the word civilization came from the *Encyclopedia of the Social Sciences,* which I have consulted on many points. The six completed volumes of Toynbee's *Study of History* have been on my desk all through the writing of this book—as is sufficiently obvious from the text. It is probably also obvious that my bias is rather different from Toynbee's (if he can be accused of having a bias) but my disagreement with some of his generalizations does not detract from my great admiration for his scholarship and for his handy way of synthesizing a mass of relevant observations into memorable and useful general concepts. I have also relied a great deal on the review of the origins of Old World civilizations given by Turner (1941).

The standard reference for Mayan civilization is the thorough and beautifully illustrated review by Morley (1946), though the older account by Gann and Thompson (1931) is perhaps better adapted to casual reading. The best general account that I know of Incan civilization is by Means (1931). The quotation is from Mangelsdorf and Reeves (1939) p. 275.

CHAPTER VI. ON TROPICAL CLIMATES

A general review of climates is contained in the *Yearbook* of the U. S. Department of Agriculture for 1941. The subject is also generally treated in textbooks of geography; the one I have consulted most frequently is by White and Renner (1948). For history of climate, there is a general summary by Brooks (1949). The best general reference from the biological point of view would be the big book by Allee and others (1949) which, because of its extensive bibliography, provides a key to a wide and scattered literature.

CHAPTER VII. CLOTHES MAKE THE MAN

My standard reference all through this chapter has been the book edited by Newburgh (1949); but this, except for the introductory chapter by Frederick Wulsin, is written in a highly technical style that makes for difficult reading. The Darwin quotation is from the *Beagle* entry for Dec. 25, 1832. My ideas about the history of clothing derive from general reading, and I find it difficult to cite specific sources. Lips (1949) includes much material on ornamentation, but not on clothing as such. The numerous histories of costume are mostly concerned with Western clothing, giving scant mention of other cultures. Hiler (1929) is an exception. My notes on Mayan dress are from Morley (1946), whence also the Bishop Landa quotation.

The account of body temperature control is based on various chapters in Newburgh (1949) and on several medical textbooks, especially Napier (1946) and Mackie and others (1945). My Adolph citation is (1938). The references in the Newburgh book provide an adequate start for anyone who wants to explore the original literature in this field, but I might also cite Lee (1950); Lee and Lemons (1949); and Sundstroem (1926 and 1927).

CHAPTER VIII. THE WHITE MAN'S BURDEN

Of Huntington's numerous books, I have read only (1924) and (1945). The extreme position, regarding tropical climate as quite hopeless for civilization, is taken by Mills (1942). Markham (1947) also takes a dim view of warm climates, though it is from his book that I got the idea of the adaptations that were necessary before civilization could move north of the Alps. The standard book on the white man in the tropics is Price (1939).

It is clear, from my text, that I am skeptical about the adaptive characteristics of human races. I feel that such adaptations are surely present, but I do not think that they have been demonstrated in the work familiar to me. The opposite point of view is developed by

Coon, Garn and Birdsell (1950) and their book probably makes a good antidote for this chapter of mine. I cite Robinson and others (1941) and Weiner (1950) as examples of the sort of careful work that has failed to show racial adaptation to climate.

A critique of the inter-racial and inter-cultural I. Q. comparisons is given by Kluckhohn (1949). A general review of the sexual behavior of man by Ford and Beach (1951) has been published since my chapter was written; this shows nicely how cultural factors overwhelm possible climatic influences. My data on African mortalities are taken from Kuczynski (1948).

I have not mentioned housing in the text, though this is prominent among the white man's burdens. The subject has been reviewed by Lee (1951).

CHAPTER IX. TROPICAL DISEASES

In writing this chapter I have most often consulted the books by Napier (1946), Mackie and others (1945) and Scott (1939). This does not mean that I consider these the best textbooks on tropical medicine: they happened to be most useful for the particular points I wanted to check. Much of this chapter is personal opinion, based on my own work on malaria and yellow fever.

CHAPTER X. FOOD AND DRINK

Careful studies of nutrition and food habits among tropical peoples are beginning to be made, and the paper by R. K. Anderson and others (1946) may be cited as an example. Thompson (1949) has given an interesting sketch of the food relations of a Fijian community, which illustrates a valuable research approach to these problems. The history of maize has been reviewed in a non-technical article by Mangelsdorf (1950) and at greater length by Mangelsdorf and Reeves (1939). The *British Medical Journal* quotation is from an anonymous editorial entitled "A Toast to Bacchus" in the issue for Dec. 23, 1950, p. 1428. Cassava and other food-plants of the American tropics have been discussed by Sauer (1950). The account of the breadfruit is based on Popenoe (1927), a book which remains the standard reference on tropical fruits. The history of citrus fruits is taken from Webber and Batchelor (1943). The autobiography of David Fairchild (1938) contains illuminating observations on tropical horticulture and agriculture.

CHAPTER XI. TROPICAL NATURE

The classical naturalists provide the best reading on tropical nature in general, and I especially recommend the books by H. W. Bates (1864), Belt (1874), Spruce (1908) and Wallace (1869). Wallace (1878) assembled some general essays on tropical nature in book form. Cutright (1940) gives a bibliography of the principal writings of naturalists on the American tropics; Worthington (1938) includes bibliographic material on Africa as do Honig and Verdoorn (1945) on Indonesia.

The statistics on species of birds are from Dobzhansky (1950). The notes on insects as food for man are from Brues (1946). The quotation on howler monkeys is from Chapman (1929).

CHAPTER XII. THE RAIN FOREST

The forest trees of tropical America have been reviewed by Record and Hess (1943), and the forestry of a single region, Trinidad, by Marshall (1939) and Beard (1946).

CHAPTER XIII. TROPICAL SEAS

The standard reference book on oceanography—tropical or otherwise—is by Sverdrup, Johnson and Fleming (1946). The problems of the origin of coral reefs have recently been reviewed by Ladd and Tracey (1949), who give a bibliography of the important books and articles.

CHAPTER XIV. THE RESOURCES OF THE TROPICS

An excellent review of the natural resources of various tropical regions has been published in a volume edited by Linton (1949). Hanson (1949) has given an enthusiastic view of the tropical possibilities of the future. The common ground between economics and anthropology has been described by Herskovits (1940). The problems of defining standards of living have been touched on by Davis (1945) and of economics and ethics in the writings of Boulding, as (1951). Some background of the history of economic.thought, such as that provided by Condliffe (1950) seems to me essential for any consideration of resource problems.

CHAPTER XV. THE VARIETIES OF TROPICAL GOVERNMENT

There is an extensive literature on colonialism and colonial policy, which I have not attempted to explore. For specific reference, I have consulted various articles in the *Encyclopedia of the Social Sciences*. The quotation on *padrões* is from Hart (1950), p. 29. The Las Casas quotation is translated from the *Historia de las Indias*.

The general problems of colonial policies have been discussed by Furnivall (1948) in his thought-provoking book on Burma and Netherlands India. The complex problems of government in Africa have been surveyed in the monumental report by Lord Hailey (1938). The colonial history of Latin America has been written by Crow (1946). A survey of contemporary nationalist movements in Asia has been given by Thompson and Adloff (1950). The volume on the Pacific by Oliver (1951) contains many illuminating accounts of colonial developments in that area.

CHAPTER XVI. THE PLANETARY NEIGHBORHOOD

My thinking about the planetary neighborhood derives rather directly from the writings of H. G. Wells. I have often consulted his *Work, Wealth and Happiness of Mankind* (1932) while writing the present book, and my concept of the abolition of distance is based directly on his *New World Order* (1940).

My comments on the philosophy of "point four" are based on a mimeographed pamphlet of the Department of State entitled *Point Four: Cooperative Program for Aid in the Development of Economically Underdeveloped Areas,* issued November, 1949 and revised December, 1949 (145 pp.).

My remarks about the relations between science and technology in this chapter have probably been oversimplified to a misleading degree in my effort to make the basic point that Western technologies, as such, may not be directly transferable to new situations. The relations between science and technology, and the roles of both in the development and orientation of Western civilization, are surely complex, and I do not want to imply that I regard technology as an incidental by-product of some basic scientific spirit. An understanding of the possible complexities of the relationships can be obtained by reading such books as those by Mumford (1934) and Hogben (1938) and by exploration in any of the various histories of science.

Illustrations

The maps and diagrams illustrating this book were prepared by Mr. Vaughn S. Gray; the other drawings by Mrs. Alma W. Froderstrom.

The map of racial distribution (p. 40) is based on the threefold classification used by Kroeber (1948, p. 133) which shows clearly enough the racial diversity of tropical peoples; the map scale is too small for more realistic subdivision. The examples of Mayan glyphs (p. 75) are taken from Gann and Thompson (1931). The diagram of atmospheric circulation (p. 92) is based upon the diagram used by Allee and others (1949, fig. 26) which in turn was based on a figure used by Fairfield Osborn in his book, *The Pacific World.* The profile of the Andean mountains (p. 97) is based on Chapman (1917, fig. 1). The Mayan scene (p. 105) is taken from the Nebaj vase, found in the Alta Vera Pas of Guatemala and figured by Morley (1946, plate 89). The Egyptian scene (p. 108) is from Breasted (1912, fig. 36). The diagram of yellow fever cycles (p. 143) is a modification of a drawing used by Strode (1951, fig. 62). The map of malaria (p. 144) is based on that used by Russell, West and Manwell (1946) with modifications suggested by Dr. Paul Russell; "high endemicity" is not precisely definable, but the map at least suggests the regions in which malaria is most important. The rain forest diagram (p. 201) is copied from Beard (1946, fig. 13). The map of the faunal areas of littoral animals (p. 222), representing Ekman's system, is based on Sverdrup, Johnson and Fleming (1946, fig. 220); and the map of the Gulf Stream (p. 225) is based on fig. 185 of the same book.

References

ADOLPH, E. F.
1938. Heat exchanges of man in the desert. American Journal of Physiology, vol. 123, pp. 486–499, 5 figs.
ALLEE, W. C., A. E. EMERSON, O. PARK, T. PARK and K. P. SCHMIDT.
1949. Principles of animal ecology. Philadelphia: W. B. Saunders Co., xii + 837 pp., 263 figs.
ANDERSON, R. K., J. CALVO, G. SERRANO and G. C. PAYNE.
1946. A study of the nutritional status and food habits of Otomi Indians in the Mezquital Valley of Mexico. American Journal of Public Health, vol. 36, pp. 883–903.
BATES, H. W.
1864. The naturalist on the River Amazons; a record of adventures, habits of animals, sketches of Brazilian and Indian life, and aspects of nature under the equator, during eleven years of travel. London: John Murray, vol. I, ix + 351 pp., 18 figs.; vol. II, vi + 423 pp., 24 figs. [A one volume edition is reprinted in "Everyman's Library."]
BATES, MARSTON.
1950. The nature of natural history. New York: Charles Scribner's Sons, 309 pp.
BATES, NANCY BELL.
1947. East of the Andes and west of nowhere; a naturalist's wife in Colombia. New York: Charles Scribner's Sons, 237 pp., 48 pls.
BEARD, J. S.
1946. The natural vegetation of Trinidad. Oxford Forestry Memoirs, No. 20. 152 pp., 46 figs.
BELT, THOMAS.
1874. The naturalist in Nicaragua; a narrative of a residence at the gold mines of Chontales; journeys in the savannahs and forests; with observations of animals and plants in reference to the theory of evolution of living forms. London:

John Murray, xvi + 403 pp., 27 figs. [Reprinted in "Every-man's Library."]

BLUNT, E. A. H.
1931. The caste system of northern India with special reference to the United Provinces of Agra and Oudh. Oxford University Press, ix + 374 pp.

BOULDING, K. E.
1951. Defense and opulence: the ethics of international economics. American Economic Review, vol. 41 (No. 2, Papers and Proceedings), pp. 210–220.

BOYD, W. C.
1950. Genetics and the races of man; an introduction to modern physical anthropology. Boston: Little, Brown & Co., xvii + 453 pp., 52 figs.

BREASTED, J. H.
1912. A history of Egypt; from the earliest times to the Persian conquest. (2nd ed.). New York: Charles Scribner's Sons, xxxi + 634 pp., 186 figs., 13 maps.

BROOKS, C. E. P.
1949. Climate through the ages; a study of the climatic factors and their variations. New York: McGraw-Hill Book Co., 395 pp., 39 figs.

BROWN, L. A.
1949. The story of maps. Boston: Little, Brown & Co., xix + 397 pp., 82 figs.

BRUES, C. T.
1946. Insect dietary; an account of the food habits of insects. Cambridge: Harvard Univ. Press, xxvi + 466 pp., 68 figs., 22 pls.

BUNBURY, E. H.
1883. A history of ancient geography among the Greeks and Romans from the earliest ages till the fall of the Roman Empire. (2nd edition). London: John Murray, vol. I, xxx + 666 pp., 10 maps; vol. II, xix + 743 pp., 10 maps.

CHAPMAN, F. M.
1917. The distribution of bird-life in Colombia; a contribution to a biological survey of South America. Bulletin of the American Museum of Natural History, vol. XXXVI; 729 pp.; 41 pls., 21 figs.

1929. My tropical air castle; nature studies in Panama. New York: D. Appleton & Co., xv + 417 pp., 46 pls., 30 figs.

CONANT, J. B.
1951. Science and common sense. New Haven: Yale Univ. Press, xii + 371 pp., 32 figs.

CONDLIFFE, J. B.
1950. The commerce of nations. New York: W. W. Norton & Co., xi + 884 pp., 16 figs.

COON, C. S., S. M. GARN and J. B. BIRDSELL.
1950. Races . . . a study of the problems of race formation in man. Springfield, Ill.: Charles C. Thomas, xiv + 153 pp., 15 pls.

CROW, J. A.
1946. The epic of Latin America. New York: Doubleday & Co., xxiv + 756 pp.

CUTRIGHT, P. R.
1940. The great naturalists explore South America. New York: Macmillan Co., xii + 340 pp., 41 figs.

DARWIN, CHARLES.
1839. Narrative of the surveying voyages of His Majesty's Ships Adventure and Beagle, between the years 1826 and 1836, describing their examination of the southern shores of South America and the Beagle's circumnavigation of the globe. Vol. III. Journal and remarks. London: Henry Colburn, xiv + 615 pp. [Reprints are usually based on the separate 1845 publication, "Journal of researches . . . ", London: John Murray.]

1842. The structure and distribution of coral reefs; being the first part of the geology of the voyage of the Beagle under the command of Capt. FitzRoy, R.N., 1832–1836. London: Smith, Elder & Co., xii + 214 pp.

1871. The descent of man and selection in relation to sex. London: John Murray, vol. I, viii + 423 pp., 25 figs.; vol. II, viii + 475 pp., 51 figs.

DAVIS, J. S.
1945. Standards and content of living. The American Economic Review, vol. 35, pp. 1–15.

DOBZHANSKY, THEODOSIUS.
1950. Evolution in the tropics. American Scientist, vol. 38, pp. 209–221, 4 figs.

FAIRCHILD, DAVID.
  1938. The world was my garden; travels of a plant explorer. New
        York: Charles Scribner's Sons, xiv + 494 pp., ill.
FORD, C. S. and F. A. BEACH.
  1951. Patterns of sexual behavior. New York: Harper & Bros.,
        viii + 307 pp., 16 figs.
FORDE, C. D.
  1934. Habitat, economy and society; a geographical introduction
        to ethnology. New York: E. P. Dutton & Co., xv + 500
        pp., 109 figs.
FURNIVALL, J. S.
  1948. Colonial policy and practice; a comparative study of
        Burma and Netherlands India. Cambridge: at the Univer-
        sity Press, xiii + 568 pp.
GANN, THOMAS and J. E. THOMPSON.
  1931. The history of the Maya from the earliest times to the
        present day. New York: Charles Scribner's Sons, x + 264
        pp., 27 pls.
GLESINGER, EGON.
  1949. The coming age of wood. New York: Simon & Schuster,
        Inc., xv + 279 pp., ill.
HAILEY, LORD [MALCOLM].
  1938. An African survey; a study of problems arising in Africa
        south of the Sahara. Oxford Univ. Press, xxviii + 1837
        pp., 6 maps.
HANSON, E. P.
  1949. New worlds emerging. New York: Duell, Sloan & Pearce,
        xix + 385 pp.
HART, H. H.
  1950. Sea road to the Indies; an account of the voyages and ex-
        ploits of the Portuguese navigators, together with the life
        and times of Dom Vasco da Gama, Capitão-Mór, Viceroy
        of India and Count of Vidigueira. New York: Macmillan
        Co., xii + 296 pp.
HERSKOVITS, M. J.
  1940. The economic life of primitive peoples. New York: Alfred
        A. Knopf, xii + 492 + xxviii pp., 1 map.
  1948. Man and his works: the science of cultural anthropology.
        New York: Alfred A. Knopf, xviii + 678 + xxxvii pp.,
        18 pls., 66 figs.

HEYERDAHL, THOR.
1950. Kon-Tiki; across the Pacific by raft. Chicago: Rand, McNally & Co., 304 pp., ill.

HILER, HILAIRE.
1929. From nudity to raiment. New York: E. Weythe, (18) + viii + 303 pp., 24 pls., 141 figs.

HOGBEN, LANCELOT.
1938. Science for the citizen; a self-educator based on the social background of scientific discovery. New York: Alfred A. Knopf, Vol. I, xiii + 532 pp.; vol. II, pp. 535–1082 + xix; ill.

HONIG, PIETER and FRANS VERDOORN (Editors).
1945. Science and scientists in the Netherlands Indies. New York: Board for the Netherlands Indies, Surinam & Curaçao, xxiv + 491 pp., 134 figs.

HOOTON, EARNEST.
1942. Man's poor relations. New York: Doubleday, Doran & Co., xl + 412 pp., 85 figs.
1947. Up from the ape. New York: Macmillan Co., xxii + 788 pp., 39 pls., 68 figs.

HUNTINGTON, ELLSWORTH.
1924. Civilization and climate (3rd edition). New Haven: Yale Univ. Press, xix + 453 pp., 48 figs.
1945. Mainsprings of civilization. New York: John Wiley & Sons, xii + 660 pp., 83 figs.

KLUCKHOHN, CLYDE.
1949. Mirror for man; the relation of anthropology to modern life. New York: Whittlesey House, xi + 313 pp.

KROEBER, A. L.
1948. Anthropology; race, language, culture, psychology, prehistory. New York: Harcourt, Brace & Co., xii + 856 + xxix pp., 42 figs.

KUCZYNSKI, R. R.
1948. Demographic survey of the British colonial empire. Vol. I, West Africa. Oxford Univ. Press, xiii + 821 pp.

LADD, H. S. and J. I. TRACEY, Jr.
1949. The problem of coral reefs. Scientific Monthly, vol. 69, pp. 297–305.

LEE, D. H. K.
  1950. Physiology as a guide to combating tropical stress. New
        England Journal of Medicine, vol. 243, pp. 723–730.
  1951. Thoughts on housing for the humid tropics. Geographical
        Review, vol. 41, pp. 124–147, 26 figs.

LEE, D. H. K. and H. LEMONS.
  1949. Clothing for global man. Geographical Review, vol. 39,
        pp. 181–213, 6 figs., 2 maps.

LINTON, RALPH (Editor).
  1949. Most of the world; the peoples of Africa, Latin America,
        and the East today. New York: Columbia Univ. Press,
        917 pp., 18 maps.

LIPS, J. E.
  1949. The origin of things; a cultural history of man. London:
        George G. Harrap & Co., 420 pp., ill.

MACKIE, T. T., G. W. HUNTER and C. B. WORTH.
  1945. A manual of tropical medicine; prepared under the
        auspices of the Division of Medical Sciences of the Na-
        tional Research Council. Philadelphia: W. B. Saunders
        Co., xix + 727 pp., 287 figs.

MANGELSDORF, P. C.
  1950. The mystery of corn. Scientific American, vol. 183, no. 1
        (July), pp. 20–24, ill.

MANGELSDORF, P. C. and R. G. REEVES.
  1939. The origin of Indian corn and its relatives. Texas Agric.
        Exp. Station Bull. no. 574, 315 pp., 95 figs.

MARKHAM, S. F.
  1947. Climate and the energy of nations. Oxford Univ. Press,
        x + 240 pp., 24 figs.

MARSHALL, R. C.
  1939. Silviculture of the trees of Trinidad and Tobago, British
        West Indes. Oxford Univ. Press, xlvii + 247 pp., 16 pls.

MEANS, P. A.
  1931. Ancient civilizations of the Andes. New York: Charles
        Scribner's Sons, xviii + 586 pp., 223 figs.
  1935. The Spanish Main: focus of envy. New York: Charles
        Scribner's Sons, xiii + 278 pp., 6 figs.

MILLS, C. A.
  1942. Climate makes the man. New York: Harper & Bros., vi +
        320 pp., 9 figs.

MONTAGU, M. F. A.
 1945. An introduction to physical anthropology. Springfield, Ill.:
  Charles C. Thomas, xiv + 325 pp., 25 figs.
MORLEY, S. G.
 1946. The ancient Maya. Stanford Univ., Calif.: Stanford Univ.
  Press, xxxii + 520 pp., 95 pls., 57 figs.
MUMFORD, LEWIS.
 1934. Technics and civilization. New York: Harcourt, Brace &
  Co., xi + 495 pp., 16 pls.
NAPIER, L. E.
 1946. The principles and practice of tropical medicine. New
  York: Macmillan Co., xvi + 917 pp., 195 figs., 24 pls.
NEWBURGH, L. H. (Editor).
 1949. Physiology of heat regulation and the science of clothing.
  Philadelphia: W. B. Saunders Co., viii + 457 pp., 78 figs.
OLIVER, D. L.
 1951. The Pacific islands. Cambridge: Harvard Univ. Press, xi +
  313 pp., 30 figs.
OSBORN, FAIRFIELD.
 1948. Our plundered planet. Boston: Little, Brown & Co., xiv +
  217 pp.
OUTHWAITE, LEONARD.
 1935. Unrolling the map; the story of exploration. New York:
  Reynal & Hitchcock, xiv + 351 pp., 56 maps.
PAYNE, E. J.
 1892. History of the New World called America. Vol. I. Oxford
  Univ. Press, xxxi + 603 pp.
POPENOE, WILSON.
 1927. Manual of tropical and subtropical fruits excluding the
  banana, coconut, pineapple, Citrus fruits, olive and fig.
  New York: Macmillan Co., xv + 474 pp., 24 pls., 62 figs.
PRICE, A. G.
 1939. White settlers in the tropics. New York: American Geogr.
  Soc., Special Publication No. 23, xiii + 311 pp., 88 figs.
RECORD, S. J. and R. W. HESS.
 1943. Timbers of the New World. New Haven: Yale Univ. Press,
  xv + 640 pp., 58 pls.
ROBINSON, S., D. B. DILL, J. W. WILSON and N. NIELSON.
 1941. Adaptations of white men and negroes to prolonged work
  in humid heat. American Journal of Tropical Medicine,
  vol. 21, pp. 261–287, 2 figs.

ROUGHLEY, T. C.
  1947. Wonders of the Great Barrier Reef. New York: Charles
        Scribner's Sons, xiii + 282 pp., 50 pls.

RUSSELL, P. F., L. S. WEST and R. D. MANWELL.
  1946. Practical Malariology. Philadelphia: W. B. Saunders Co.,
        xx + 684 pp., 238 figs.

SAUER, C. O.
  1950. Cultivated plants of South and Central America *in* J. H.
        Steward, "Handbook of South American Indians," vol. 6,
        pp. 487–543.

SCOTT, H. H.
  1939. A history of tropical medicine. Baltimore: Williams &
        Wilkins Co., vol. I, xix + 648 pp.; vol. II, pp. 649–1219;
        13 pls.

SIMPSON, G. G.
  1949. The meaning of evolution; a study of the history of life
        and of its significance for man. New Haven: Yale Univ.
        Press, xv + 364 pp., 38 figs.

SPRUCE, RICHARD.
  1908. Notes of a botanist on the Amazon and Andes. (Edited
        and condensed by Alfred Russel Wallace.) London: Mac-
        millan & Co., vol. I, lii + 518 pp., 49 figs., 3 maps; vol. II,
        xii + 542 pp., 22 figs., 4 maps.

STEFANSSON, VILHJALMUR (Editor).
  1947. Great adventures and explorations; from the earliest times
        to the present, as told by the explorers themselves. New
        York: Dial Press, xii + 788 pp., 18 maps.

STEWARD, J. H. (Editor).
  1946–1950. Handbook of South American Indians. Washington:
        U. S. Gov. Printing Office, vol. I (1946), the marginal
        tribes, xix + 624 pp., 112 pls., 69 figs., 7 maps; vol. II
        (1946), the Andean civilizations, xxxiv + 1035 pp., 192
        pls., 100 figs., 11 maps; vol. III (1948), the tropical forest
        tribes, xxvi + 986 pp., 126 pls., 134 figs., 8 maps; vol. IV
        (1948) the circum-Caribbean tribes, xx + 609 pp., 98 pls.,
        79 figs., 11 maps; vol. V (1949), the comparative ethnol-
        ogy of South American Indians, xxvi + 818 pp., 56 pls.,
        190 figs., 22 maps; vol. VI (1950), physical anthropology,

linguistics and cultural geography of South American Indians, xiii + 715 pp., 47 pls., 3 figs., 18 maps.

STRODE, G. K. (Editor).
    1951. Yellow fever. New York: McGraw-Hill Book Co., xv + 710 pp., 77 figs.

SUNDSTROEM, E. S.
    1926. Contributions to tropical physiology with special reference to the adaptation of the white man to the climate of north Queensland. Univ. of California Publications in Physiology, vol 6, pp. 1–216, 26 figs.
    1927. The physiological effects of tropical climate. Physiological Reviews, vol. 7, pp. 320–362.

SVERDRUP, H. U., M. W. JOHNSON and R. H. FLEMING.
    1946. The oceans: their physics, chemistry and general biology. New York: Prentice-Hall, Inc., x + 1087 pp., 265 figs., 7 charts.

THOMPSON, LAURA.
    1949. The relations of men, animals and plants in an island community (Fiji). American Anthropologist, vol. 51, pp. 253–267.

THOMPSON, VIRGINIA and RICHARD ADLOFF.
    1950. The left wing in southeast Asia. New York: Wm. Sloane Associates, xiv + 298 pp., 13 figs.

TOYNBEE, A. J.
    1934–1939. A study of history. Oxford Univ. Press, vol. I (1934), xvi + 476 pp; vol. II (1934), vii + 452 pp.; vol. III (1934), vi + 551 pp.; vol. IV (1939), xvi + 656 pp.; vol. V (1939), vi + 712 pp.; vol. VI (1939), vi + 633 pp.

TURNER, RALPH.
    1941. The great cultural traditions; the foundations of civilizations. Vol. I, the ancient cities. New York: McGraw-Hill, xviii + 601 + xxiv pp., ill.

TYLOR, E. B.
    1871. Primitive culture; researches into the development of mythology, philosophy, religion, language, art and custom. London: John Murray.

UNITED STATES DEPARTMENT OF AGRICULTURE.
    1941. Yearbook of agriculture; climate and man. Washington: U. S. Gov. Printing Office, xii + 1248 pp., ill.

VOGT, WILLIAM.
  1948. Road to survival. New York: Wm. Sloane Associates,
        xvi + 335 pp., ill.
VON HAGEN, V. W.
  1945. South America called them; explorations of the great
        naturalists, La Condamine, Humboldt, Darwin, Spruce.
        New York: Alfred A. Knopf, xii + 311 + ix pp., 28 figs.
WALLACE, A. R.
  1869. The Malay Archipelago; the land of the orang-utan, and
        the bird of paradise; a narrative of travel, with studies of
        man and nature. London: Macmillan & Co., vol. I, xix +
        312 pp., 27 figs.; vol. II, 341 pp., 24 figs.
  1878. Tropical nature and other essays. London: Macmillan
        Co., xiii + 356 pp.
WEBBER, H. J. and L. D. BATCHELOR (Editors).
  1943. The Citrus industry. Vol. I, history, botany and breeding.
        Berkeley: Univ. of California Press, xx + 1028 pp., 233
        figs.
WEINER, J. S.
  1950. Observations on the working ability of Bantu mineworkers
        with reference to acclimatization to hot humid conditions.
        British Journal of Industrial Medicine, vol. 7, pp. 17–26,
        3 figs.
WELLS, H. G.
  1931. The work, wealth and happiness of mankind. New York:
        Doubleday, Doran & Co., vol. I, xvi + 454 pp.; vol. II,
        pp. 457–924; ill.
  1940. The new world order; whether it is attainable, how it can
        be attained, and what sort of a world a world at peace will
        have to be. New York: Alfred A. Knopf, 145 pp.
WHITE, C. L. and G. T. RENNER.
  1948. Human geography; an ecological study of society. New
        York: Appleton-Century-Crofts, Inc., x + 692 pp., ill.
WISER, C. V. and W. H. WISER.
  1930. Behind mud walls. New York: Richard Smith, Inc., xi +
        180 pp.
WORTHINGTON, E. B.
  1938. Science in Africa; a review of scientific research relating
        to tropical and southern Africa. Oxford Univ. Press, xv +
        746 pp., 8 pls., 5 maps.

WRIGHT, J. K.

    1925. The geographical lore of the time of the crusades; a study in the history of medieval science and tradition in western Europe. New York: American Geogr. Soc., xxi + 563 pp., ill.

Index

Abyssinia, 58, 70, 171; *see also* Ethiopia
Acacia, 187
Activity and climate, 122
Adaptations to heat, 113
Adloff, Richard, 284
Adolph, E. F., 110, 281
Aedes aegypti, 140–143
Aeta, 53
Africa, civilization in, 42, 83, 162
  colonies in, 251, 258
  disease in, 126, 127, 130
  effect of European contact, 24
  food-gathering cultures of, 54
  government in, 258
  human fossils in, 34
  iron-working in, 62
  pastoral cultures in, 60
  races of, 41
  spread of sleeping sickness, 148
Africanthropus, 34
Agriculture, of Incas, 59, 76
  origins of, 52–61
  periods of, 59
  potentialities of, 238
  in tropics, 55, 240
Ainu race, 45
Air conditioning, 121
Air plants, 183–185
Akbar, 166, 167
Albania, disease in, 136
Alcoholic drinks, *see* Fermented drinks
Alexander VI, Pope, 250
Algae, 215, 220
Allee, W. C., 281, 286
Almeida, Francesco d', 250
Alpaca, 77
Altitude and climate, 96, 97
  of tropical cities, 127

Aluminum, 236
Amazon, 27, 28, 54, 94, 178, 186, 206, 243
America, agriculture in, 56
  absence of human fossils in, 33
  antiquity of man in, 36, 261
  civilization in, 71–79
  colonies in, 251
  effect of European contact in, 23
  races in, 40
  see also Latin America
Amerind as race name, 39
Amoebic dysentery, 150
Anaconda, 190
Andean civilization, 62, 68, 74–78; *see also* Incas
Andes mountains, 58, 95–97
Anderson, R. K., 282
Angkor Thom, 81
Angola, 237
Animal domestication, 59–61
Annam, 247, 257
Anona, 169, 170
Anopheles, 139, 146
Antarctica, 88, 175
Anteater, 203
Anthropoidea, 32
Ants, 187, 189, 199
Anuradhapura, 80
Apes, 32, 193
Arabic civilization, 61, 68
Arctic type clothing, 103
Argentina, 246
Arid climate, 79, 94, 95
Aristarchus, 12
Aroids, 184
Artocarpus incisa, 163
Aryans, 4, 43, 49
Asia, civilizations of, 79–84

Mexico City, 127
Miami, 86
Microclimate, 98
Mills, C. A., 281
Mimicry, 187
Minoan civilization, 68, 69
Modjokerto child, 33
Mohammedanism, 24, 80, 171
Mongolian or Mongoloid race, 39, 40, 43, 44
Monkeys, 192, 193, 203
Monroe, President, 266
Monsoon climate, 94
Montagu, M. F. A., 279
Moriche palm, 181
Morley, S. G., 73, 105, 280, 281, 286
Morpho, 186
Mosquitoes, breeding places, 208
  and dermatobia, 152
  and filaria, 138
  immunity to bites of, 131
  and malaria, 145–147
  in New Jersey, 207
  in Villavicencio, 207
  and yellow fever, 140–143
Mosses, 183, 185
Motilone Indians, 41, 209
Mountain climates, 95–97
Mozambique, 21
Mumford, Lewis, 285
Mumps, 129

Nagana, 147
Napier, L. E., 281, 282
Nasca culture, 76
Natal, 21
Nationalism, 252–258
Natives, attitude towards, 119, 132
Natural history, 6
Naturalist, point of view of, 5
Neanderthal man, 32, 34
Necho, Pharaoh, 17
Negro races, 41, 45
Negritos, 53
Nekton, 213
Newburgh, L. H., 108, 116, 281
Newfoundland, 178
New Guinea, 28, 177, 186

New Haven, 3
New Jersey, 89, 207
New York, 31, 135, 178
New Zealand, 177, 226
Niches of tropical forest, 207
Nigeria, 142
Nile, 5, 70, 89
North Carolina, 125
Nutmeg, 237
Nutrition and culture, 154–156

Obliquity of the ecliptic, 11
Oceania, races of, 44
Oceans, 221–224
Oikoumene, 14, 15, 80
Oil, 235, 236
Oliver, Douglas, 44, 278, 279, 284
Olympic mountains, rainfall, 198
Opium, 174
Opossums, 203
Orange, 165, 166
Orangutans, 193
Orchids, 183–185
Orinoco, 28, 54, 95, 181
Orthodox civilization, 68, 71
Osborn, Fairfield, 92, 238, 286
Ottoman Empire, 19
Outhwaite, Leonard, 278
Oviedo y Valdés, Gonzalo Fernandez de, 26, 29, 161
Oysters, 188

Pacific Islands, races of, 44
Padrões, 249
Pakistan, 246, 257
Paleface as racial name, 39
Palms, 180–182
Palm viper, 189
Palolo worms, 227
Papuan race, 44
Panama, 1, 31, 97, 141, 178, 191
Papaya, 169
Paraguay, 174
Páramo zone, 96
Parasites vs. epiphytes, 183
Pastoral cultures, 60
Payne, E. J., 55
Peanuts, 77, 237
Pejibaye palm, 182